TO NASA
& BEYOND

TO NASA & BEYOND

Perseverance to Achieve the Impossible

KEVIN J DEBRUIN

Originally self-published by DeBruin Enterprises, LLC printed in paperback by Amazon, 2019.

Self-published simultaneously by DeBruin Enterprises, LLC printed in paperback by Ingram Content Group, 2019.

Exterior image credits: front cover, credit: Sebastian Leon; front cover Europa, credit: NASA/Galileo; front cover Jupiter image, credit: Purchased for use by Sebastian Leon; back cover design, credit: Sebastian Leon.

Interior image credits: Fit Rocket Scientist logo brainstorming and creation, credit: Brandon Frederickson. Logo copyright © 2018 by Kevin J DeBruin.

IBSN: 978-0-578-46606-4

Library of Congress Control Number: 2019902022

Published 2019

Printed in the United States of America

CONTENTS

PART 1
NASA OR BUST

Holy Crap I'm at NASA!

AS YOU APPROACH the entrance to NASA JPL you see the large NASA meatball logo and a typography that reads "WELCOME TO OUR UNIVERSE". The meatball logo is a blue ball with white NASA letters in the center, speckled stars in the background, a white ellipse in the center and two red lines like a skinny flying pyramid going from the bottom left to the top right. The blue sphere represents a planet, the stars represent space, the red chevron is a wing representing aeronautics (the latest design in hypersonic wings at the time the logo was developed), and then there is an orbiting spacecraft going around the wing. Driving up to JPL, seeing the giant NASA and JPL signs, gave me an extraordinary feeling. Wow, I was at NASA JPL for the first time!

Only a couple days ago I was at my house in Atlanta. I grabbed my backpack, duffle bag, and suit carrier and started walking to the train station to bring me to the airport. I packed along a few extra items that I thought would bring me good energy during the interview. I brought along the VHS version of

October Sky and also my paperback copy of *Rocket Boys*. I planned on carrying these around in my backpack during my interview. Having them with me would give me a sense of security and companionship. Every time school was tough, finals approached, or I needed a pick-me-up refresher of inspiration, I watched the movie or started reading the book again. They have been with me every step of my journey thus far so it just seemed fitting to have them with me as I approached the final leg.

I boarded my plane which had a 2-3-2 seat configuration. I was the left aisle seat of the middle three seats. I sat next to a very nice lady with whom I conversed while going through and checking my presentation to ensure everything was perfect to the T. She asked me what I was doing and I gave her the rundown that was on my way to interview for my dream job and quickly told her my story of my October Sky inspiration. We kept chatting for a while and she said my mother must be very proud and she raised a fantastic son. I couldn't help but smile and said I would pass along those compliments to my mother. She also said that there was no doubt in her mind that I would rock the interview and get the job. Another great feeling of someone whom I just met could see the passion inside of me and have a sense that I would accomplish what I set out to do. For some reason everyone on the flight got free margaritas and I happily gave mine to her. I was starting to try and cut out alcohol and definitely didn't want anything disrupting my thinking at this time. I'll save my story about alcohol for another time, but I eventually stopped drinking 100% of the time and as I write this I am over four years sober without a drop.

As I exited the plane, the woman who sat next to me wished me the best of luck, and I was off to collect my luggage and get my rental car. This was my first time in California since a trip I took with my Boy Scout troop when I was 14-years old. Ever since that trip I knew I wanted to live in California. We spent two days in Joshua Tree desert, two days in the San Bernardino mountains, and then a few days on Laguna Beach. To experience all three environments within driving distance, I knew this is was where I wanted to end up. Now it is 11 years later and I am trying to make that dream a reality.

I had never been to Pasadena specifically, but I had a picture in my mind of what it would be like. Driving to the hotel from the airport I finally was able to see it. Pasadena was exactly what I pictured in my mind. The streets were lined with tall palm trees, a main downtown street full of shops and heavy foot traffic. There were little houses with gorgeous landscaping and multiple apartments and condos along the way.

I arrived at the hotel, unpacked, and headed to the hotel gym for a workout after a day of sitting on a train and flying. It was about 5 or 6 o'clock in the evening California time, but coming from Atlanta it was 8 or 9 o'clock in the evening time to my body. My interview was set for 8am, which was more like 11am for me. The time zone was going to make this a little tricky. I normally wake up at about 6am EST, so I would be up at 3am PST. A workout now would help me stay up a little later so I could maybe sleep like I was in the Western Time zone. I knew that I had an 8-hour interview in front of me the next day and that towards the later part, I was most likely going to be struggling since I would be up so early. Caffeine was going to be a must to help me out.

I woke up around 4 or 5 o'clock in the morning local time. I used this time to practice my presentation again, review my interview questions, and other reference material. I practiced my presentation twice, maybe even three times, to keep it fresh. I wanted to be at the top of my game and I was feeling tired from travels and the time change. I used one of the hotel coffee cups and actually mixed my pre-workout powder in some water and poured it in. I chose the pre-workout over coffee because the one I had packed a 300mg punch of caffeine; about double that of a large coffee. I could sip this slowly throughout my interview and feel pretty good. And yes, I put it in the coffee cup for appearances. I could have used my water bottle, but then I wouldn't have water if I wanted a drink without caffeine and a coffee cup in hand just gave the appearance I was looking for.

I arrived at JPL, parked in the visitor's lot as instructed by the guard, and headed into the Visitor Center. Dressed to the nine walking into the Visitor Center, my stride and smile showed excitement and confidence. There were two other people there to interview as well. I sat down and introduced myself to them and struck up conversation on who we were, where we were from, and what inspired us to get into space. It turned out that none of us were interviewing with the same sections, so we had no competition in each other. That made for a friendlier environment. We received our interview schedules and each went our separate ways for our interviews, but would be brought together again for a lab tour in the afternoon. The interview day had officially started. Holy crap... how did I get here?

A Defining Moment

I BECAME A NASA Rocket Scientist without ever taking a space course in school. Seriously. Let that sink in for a second. This is not a tale of deception, but a story of perseverance.

It wasn't until I was hit with rejection after rejection from several institutions that I learned the definition and benefit of persistence. Through those rejections I discovered what I was made of, what I was capable of, and what I would be willing to do to achieve my dream. My experiences taught me that rejection means nothing if you are truly passionate about something. This mindset is what enabled me to get accepted into every institution that rejected me. I realized anyone can make it happen no matter what you are told, no matter what happens. When you wholeheartedly believe you are meant to do something, there is nothing that can stand in your way. This is my journey to NASA…& Beyond.

What defines your life? What is your "why"? What drives you, gives you motivation, keeps you going when you think everything is falling apart? My journey to NASA started by watching the movie *October Sky* as a ten year old boy. The movie played on a television in the middle of a large wooden entertainment center nestled between a fish tank and a stack of books. I was captivated by this movie. *October Sky* is based on the book *Rocket Boys* by Homer Hickam. It recounts the true story of a young man in a coal mining town in West Virginia who sees the first man-made satellite, Sputnik, streak across the night sky. This event inspired him to build rockets; even blowing up his mom's fence once. He overcame adversity from his town's judgement and his unsupportive father to achieve his dream. Homer became a NASA Engineer training astronauts. Watching this movie gave me a moment of happiness that was all too rare. Life seemed great from the outside, but many did not know the internal struggles of my family.

I sat there cross-legged on the living room carpet with my curly red hair, wearing a red power ranger shirt, and had my eyes laser-locked on the TV. My focus on this movie was unshakable. I was awestruck by this story for its incredible display of rocketry and its ability to relate to crucial aspects of my life. I too had a struggling relationship with my father. Witnessing a young man with similar difficulties achieve success, showed me that I too could accomplish my dreams whatever they may be. It was right then and there that the mindset of "space or bust" was instilled within me. I knew at that exact moment I had a strong desire to work in the aerospace industry. I remember thinking to myself, "Man, how cool would it be to design spaceships?!" Little did I know that my journey would be long, extremely tough, and disappointing at times. Ultimately ending with me doing exactly what I set out to do as a ten year old boy.

Even as early as preschool I had a strong idea of what I wanted to be. I recall when we were asked what we wanted to be when we grew up. A lot of the kids said movie star, singer, football player, basketball player, or another athlete; but not me and my partner Marcus. The teacher put us in pairs to start creating positive friendships. Marcus was friendly, and showed that with a great big smile. He was one of the shorter kids at preschool and had black squiggly short hair. Marcus excitedly said he wanted to be a firefighter and I jumped up shouting out that I wanted to be an astronaut! At such a young age the fascination of outer space and spaceships was clear.

In my bedroom I had those glow-in-the-dark stars you could stick to your ceiling. I plastered them all over the place! I particularly remember having them on the ceiling fan blades. This made for an amazing view. Turn the fan on, turn the lights off, and watch the stars fly in circles over and over again. I had created my own shooting stars! One of my favorite parts of the day was right before bed. My parents would say goodnight, turn off the lights, and I would just stare up at those wondrous glowing stars. It was my own universe I was looking up at. It was unique to just me. I created it and enjoyed getting lost in its essence.

By having that desire as a boy, I knew that education was going to be important for what I wanted to do early on. I put mounds of effort into my schoolwork because I saw it as a crucial portion of my journey to becoming what I wanted to be when I grew up. Most kids were focusing on goofing off in school, seeing what they could get away with, or just not wanting to be there. Don't get me wrong, I had my fair share of goofing off and having fun too, but my first priority was acquiring knowledge. In the first grade I was part of a special English class. I do not remember why or how I got selected for it, but what I do recall is that we did "more advanced" literacy practices. "More advanced" as a first grader was reading *Winnie-the-Pooh* out loud while I'm not sure what was happening in the regular class with everyone else.

Third grade was known for two main things at my school: a homemade jeopardy game and a solar system project. The jeopardy game was an old vacuum cleaner that our teacher turned into a device with a light on top and wired controllers for the buzzers. It was a great way to get us to want to learn—turn it into a game! It was the solar system project that got me most excited, obviously. We each got to pick a planet to learn about and create a model of that chosen planet to hang from the ceiling in the classroom as we created the solar system. I picked the planet Pluto, which nowadays isn't a declared a normal planet anymore. Pluto was downgraded to a dwarf planet in 2006. I was so excited to learn about the solar system, the planets, and create my own model. I have a snapshot image in my memory of the third grade classroom. The lights were off and I was sitting in my desk towards the back of the room, gazing up at the class-created planets in the solar system formation. Much like me gazing up into the glow-in-the-dark star universe of my bedroom ceiling.

Entering middle school, going into the 6th grade, I was placed into an accelerated math class. There were about eight members of this class that would go to a separate room to learn while the remainder of our classmates stayed with the homeroom teacher. This accelerated math class would continue through 7th and 8th grade. I knew that being in this class could boost me ahead for my high school courses. I also felt some confidence in being selected as I felt like one of the "smart kids" and it made me happy. I did find this class quite challenging at times. There came a time in 7th grade when the teacher actually called a meeting with my parents because I was only earning a C grade level. She thought it may be in my best interest to leave the accelerated class. I was scared and disappointed. In the meeting, I begged the teacher not to remove me; that I wanted to be there and would try harder. She agreed to let me stay and I was relieved, but knew I had a tough time ahead of me.

I was truly struggling. It was hard and I didn't fully understand everything as quickly as the others. We would move on to another topic and I was still grasping to comprehend what we just discussed. I had to put in extra time outside of class to catch myself up. This taught me that not everything will be easy for me; that this journey would not be a walk in the park. Until this point, I pretty much didn't have to put in any additional work to maintain my academics. I was able to understand most subjects and concepts pretty well at a first take. But here in the accelerated math class, I was having a hard time understanding these new concepts. Math was something that I was always good at, but I struggled throughout this time.

The next academic battle was again with math, a subject that I thought was my strong suit. All NASA rocket scientists are geniuses and naturally good at math right? Not the case. It was now high school and I was not on the path to take calculus in my senior year. I was just a freshman, but I figured out I wouldn't be able to make it to Advanced Placement (AP) Calculus before graduation. The only way for me to get on track for Calculus was to take a summer school math class. I took geometry over the summer and my brother did as well. His name is Michael and he is 15-months older than me. Unfortunately, we were not able to take the same class because there was not enough room. We ended up at two different schools. In hindsight, this was actually a good thing. We were in a math class together later in high school. I went back to that teacher's classroom a few years ago to catch up and she told me that she loved us, but never wanted siblings in a class together again. She said this kind heartedly with a laugh. Michael and I caused some ruckus during class as any two brothers would. At the same time we always got our work done and received good grades, of course.

I give my brother the utmost respect for putting up with me during this time. I seemed to understand the concepts more quickly and get my work done easily, where he had to put in more time to understand and finish the assignments. This is part of what lead to our teacher not wanting siblings again—I would finish my work, or quickly understand what she was teaching, and then I would goof around or distract Michael. But Michael is a resilient and patient individual. He was dedicated to learning and getting his stuff done no matter what kind of distraction I would impose throughout the semester.

I was successful in the summer geometry class and got myself into AP Calculus for the last semester of high school. I made it, but once I was in the class I realized my workload was quite heavy and there was some (okay, maybe a lot of) senioritis in my system. I was already enrolled in CAPP (College accredited courses) for English and Spanish, and the date of graduation was quickly approaching. I wasn't enjoying my last semester and opted out of taking the AP test for Calculus about halfway through. This was definitely a moment of laziness, but everyone makes mistakes. Not the best move for someone trying to be a NASA rocket scientist. To work for NASA you don't have to be perfect, but you do need to make up for your mistakes. I stayed with the class, continued learning, did my homework, and took the in-class exams. The only portion outside of AP calculus that I did not complete was the 4-hour exam that may have granted me college credit. Since I opted out of this exam, I was only allowed to enroll in Pre-Calculus as a college freshman.

I could have studied and taken a math entrance exam in the summer to get myself into Calculus, but now I actually saw an opportunity to make a weaknesses a strength. I realized that if I took Pre-Calculus again I would strengthen the foundation on which everything was to follow. I had a base solidly built with Pre-Calculus and AP Calculus (without the exam) from high school, but I knew it could be stronger. Every math course that followed would rely on the principles and concepts from these foundational courses. So I made the decision to stay where I was and take Pre-Calculus again. As I am today, I have taken six more advanced math courses past Calculus I. I think it can be safely said that after these struggles, I have achieved my academic mathematical success.

From the outside my family looked perfect. My father made a lot of money, we lived in a nice house with an indoor pool, and went to Disney World a few times for family vacations. I had my older brother Michael that was adopted from Peru and in 1999 we expanded our family with a new baby sister. Her name is Elise and she was adopted from Guatemala. We had a great family, or so it seemed to others. What they didn't know was that on the inside it was full of turmoil. Anger, sadness, and abuse from my father ravaged our family.

When I was in the fourth grade, my mom found the strength to leave my father; she got a divorce to protect her children and herself from him. She is my number one hero. About one year later she met one of the best father figures there could be, Mike. And seven years later they joined hands in marriage. For the remainder of this book, and in my everyday life, when I say dad, I mean my step-dad. He was, and still is, my true father in raising and supporting my siblings and I. The combination of my number one hero, mom, and true father, Mike, is the reason I am where I am and who I am today. If anyone deserves credit for my accomplishments, may it all go to them.

Where I am from, growing up with divorced parents was only on the brink of becoming acceptable. Not many divorces occurred in my town in the early 2000's, but today they are as common as getting a new car. I struggled with having two families. This meant having two Christmases and bouncing between parental visits ordered by the judge. I saw the lack of connection between Homer and his father in *October Sky* as a relatable aspect to my life. Homer overcame it to achieve his dreams, and I knew I could do it too. Homer and his father were able to reconcile their differences. My path, however, was to abandon my previous father and connect with my dad Mike. Eliminating the negative and focusing on the positive was something I learned at a very young age. This piece of knowledge really helped pave the way for my journey ahead.

I knew where I wanted to go, but I did not know how I would get there. It was only when I started facing continued rejection in college that I finally learned how difficult it was actually going to be.

3

A Taste of Aerospace

PLATTEVILLE IS A small, agricultural town in southwest Wisconsin. It is about an hour south of the capital Madison and only a short 30 minute drive to Dubuque, Iowa. Platteville has a very small town feel, except for the Walmart that was at the edge of town right next to the highway. Tractors, farmland, and the Amish were a common sighting in this area. While walking the campus on a tour of the University of Wisconsin-Platteville, it just felt right. A feeling of "this is where I'm supposed to be" is why I chose UW-Platteville for my undergraduate college career. It's there I would pursue a Bachelor's Degree in Mechanical Engineering. It kind of reminded me of my home town Kaukauna, WI. Kaukauna has just 12,000 people and multiple farms throughout the area. The larger cities of Green Bay and Appleton are just a short drive away. I cannot put it into too many words, but it was a comfortable feeling; I knew this was the right place for the next chapter of my life.

During my third semester I found myself walking through Ullsvik Hall which had an exterior that resembled the Sydney

Opera House. I noticed a flyer for the upcoming career fair on the wall of the hallway leading to my General Business class. I didn't think too much of it at the time since I had a solid job with a landscaping company back home. I enjoyed getting in good workouts during the summer months and building elaborate waterfalls. When I got back to my dorm after class, my mind wandered back to the flyer I had seen earlier. I was a little curious so I sat down at my computer and went to the career fair website.

As I started to look through the companies that were going to be there, I began to think that maybe it was about time I tried to get myself some experience as an engineer. As I searched through the companies, I was paying attention to the "Industry" and "Interested Majors" marked columns of the table. As I approached the end of the list, I didn't see anything that really interested me. There were food processing plants, industrial metal companies, and agricultural companies such as John Deere. Then at the end I saw a company named Woodward Governor (now Woodward, Inc.) that had "AEROSPACE" listed under the "Industry" column. This was the first and only aerospace company at the career fair. Upon seeing this I launched forward in my chair and thought "Oh wow, that's it!" and immediately started researching the company.

Woodward designs fuel controls for jet turbine engines. That...sounded...awesome! At that moment, I decided that an internship at Woodward was going to be my first step in the aerospace industry. It was the only company I planned to talk to at the career fair and I invested all of my time and effort for the next three weeks to prepare for that event.

I went to the company's website that was headed with WOODWARD GOVERNOR in a deep red color surrounded with pictures of aircraft and helicopter engine parts. I read every single word on every single page. Each time I finished a paragraph, I felt my excitement building even more about working for this company. They assisted in designing engines for fighter jets, other military planes and helicopters, and even commercial aviation! Wow! I wanted to become an expert in what the company did so that I could have a strong and informative conversation with their representatives at the career fair.

The main material for a career fair is a resume. At this point I did not have a good one, or a complete one for that matter. I had a simple one from high school that I had used to apply for scholarships and colleges. It looked pretty bare and unimpressive. I knew I needed help if I wanted my resume to be competitive among the other applicants. I went to the career center to schedule an appointment with one of the career counselors. I came back for the appointment and met with Jeff R. When I knocked on his door, he stood up from behind a large wooden glossy desk. He was wearing a white colored shirt and a Winnie-the-Pooh tie. Mr. R was a tall, smiling man with a kind voice saying "Come on in, welcome Kevin. How can I help you out today?" I told him why I was there, "to get an Internship with Woodward because I want to work in aerospace", and he asked for my current resume. I handed it over, he took out a red pen, and we started walking through it. By the end, there was definitely more red ink than black ink on the paper. I couldn't even recognize that it was my resume! I took my critiqued resume back to my room along with a few handouts on resume format and writing with a drive within me to make it better. I went back about three or four times to the generous Mr. R to iterate on my resume until the career fair. After a few visits I was calling him Jeff and we had become good friends, like two colleagues working towards the same goal. He also became a reference of mine for both my NASA internship applications and my application to Georgia Tech. Jeff told me that he had written a book of exciting adventures and was known as Mr. Fun! Working on my resume was tough work, but he did make it enjoyable and fun. The name was quite fitting for him and now the Winnie-the-Pooh tie made sense.

As the career fair approached, I wanted to look professional to make a good first impression so I needed a suit coat and tie. I do not believe that before that day I had ever wore a suit coat. It was something that adults wore and I did not feel that I was there yet, I was still having fun being a kid! I asked a few friends if they had one I could use and tried to find one at the local thrift store without luck. I ended up borrowing a suit coat from a friend's neighbor in a nearby town who was a mortician.

He had a plethora of suit coats to choose from. It was almost like he bought an entire department store. Suit coats ranging from plaid, to stripes, to solid colors. I was just interested in a plain black suit, nothing too special, just the standard business look. All of these coats were sized for him at 6'2". Since I'm 6'4" it was quite a difficult task to find something that would appear to fit reasonably. The suit coat was a few inches too short in the sleeve, but it looked normal if I had my hands clasped in front of me. With my arms straight down at my sides it was obvious that I needed a longer suit coat. So I knew I would try to avoid that position whenever possible. It would have to do because the career fair was tomorrow.

I walked into the career fair dressed to the nines! Looking good, feeling good, and ready to tackle the task ahead. Actually, it wasn't quite like that at all. I was really quite nervous, felt I looked too big for my outfit, and definitely had sweaty palms. I had on the black suit coat whose sleeves were too short, a bright red power tie as recommended by Jeff, black slacks with black belt and silver buckle, and not too shiny black dress shoes. I didn't want to sound nervous talking to the Woodward reps. Luckily, I had a friend who was a rep at another booth. I decided to go talk to her and try to get my first career fair jitters out. Part of it was the excitement of what possibilities could come from a conversation with Woodard. I went over to the Woodward booth and waited my turn in line. There is a trick to help with the sweaty palms: put kleenex in the suit coat pocket and before approaching to shake hands with someone, reach into your pocket and squeeze the kleenex to dry your hands. When I got to the front, I handed my extremely revised resume over to a man named Marvin and shook his hand firmly with my newly dried palm.

Marvin had the look of a professional engineer: glasses, comb-parted black hair, plain blue collared shirt, and slacks. He had a soft, friendly face that appeared approachable. I told him about my *October Sky* motivation to show that I was passionate about the industry and not just looking for a job. I asked him what he was currently working on and what a typical intern project could be for someone of my level. I explicitly remember him telling me about soil testing of engine fuel. This struck me as odd because I didn't know why they would do such a thing and didn't know exactly what soil testing of fuel was. So I asked questions to investigate and show that I wanted to learn. Soil testing of fuel is essentially taking clean fuel and purposely mixing different amounts of soil into it before running it through the engine parts. They do this to design their fuel controls to be able to operate efficiently even with dirty fuel, making them resilient to the inputs to their system. The conversation seemed to fly by. I walked away smiling and feeling great! We had an intellectual conversation and I showed initiative by asking further detailed questions about topics he discussed. I was filled with excitement and potential, now I had to wait and hope to hear back in a couple weeks.

A few weeks later, I received a call at 8am that woke up both me and my roommate Dan. It almost startled us out of our beds. Dan and I have been best friends since high school where we played soccer together and led our team to the state playoffs our junior year. He is a giant like me also standing at 6'4", but with brown hair and a soccer player build. Dan looked over at me across our small 10'x15' dorm room from his lofted bed. We each had lofted beds where we only had about two feet of clearance to the ceiling. Both of us thinking, "Who the heck is calling at 8am?!" Something must be wrong or important so I answered with a groggy voice of "Hello?" and then heard the response "Hi, this is Lisa from Woodward Governor." I instantly became alert and gained clarity saying "Hi, how are you doing today?" I covered the microphone and told Dan it was the company I talked to at the career fair. The phone call was to invite me for an on-site interview. I was currently in Platteville, WI and the company was located in Rockford,

IL which is about two hours east by car. I asked about a Saturday morning because I could easily find a ride to spend the weekend over there, but she said that was not a possibility. Lisa said the interview needed to be on a weekday and I started to worry because I did not have a car. Dan did have a car, but was possessive of it and never let anyone drive it. I looked over to Dan, who had of course been listening, not knowing what to do and without hesitation he said that he would let me use his car. What a guy, two points for Dan!

I had the interview on Friday of the next week. I parked right in front of Woodward's massive tan brick building with a large green lawn in front of a U-shaped driveway. I was nervous and made sure to have kleenex in my pockets again. I met with Marvin, the man who interviewed me at the career fair, and he gave me a tour of the facility to start out. I was shown the assembly floor from an overlook where I was able to see numerous machines and assembly lines actually building the jet engine fuel controls! The last stop on the tour was the Woodward Museum. It was a glass room consisting of their most famous products showcasing the evolution from mechanically to electrically controlled systems. The main piece was a jet engine model in the center of the room with descriptive callouts of the components. It showed how the engine worked as a whole: taking in air, combusting it in a chamber with fuel, and exiting through a nozzle to create thrust. I wanted to stay in that room for hours and keep asking questions and learning, but I needed to continue the interview process.

I was scheduled to meet with two others. The first was a lady, a colleague of Marvin who shared a similar friendly face and kind attitude. She asked me about my schooling and what my interests and career plans were. The conversation flowed easily and was enjoyable. The nerves I had before now seemed to have disappeared and I was enjoying myself with confidence. Lastly, I met with a human resources representative that asked me the basic interview questions like: Where do you see yourself in 5, 10 years? What are your strengths/weaknesses? That interview seemed dry, but I still felt that I nailed it! I left Woodward feeling confident and excited, just like the career fair, but this time I wasn't just going to wait. I followed up that exact night with emails to the three people that interviewed me with a thank you and reiterated my skills and my interest for the job.

A few weeks later, I received a phone call in the evening from my mother. She said "So did they call you?" I replied with "Who was supposed to call me?" She said Woodward called my home number in Kaukauna looking for me and she directed them to call my cell. I said "Nope not yet, what's up?" She told me to hang up with her and await their call. I did that immediately and just a moment later the phone rang again. This time it was Woodward offering me an internship! Of course I accepted it and literally jumped for joy in my dorm room before running down the hallways with excitement. I hugged Dan thanking him for his help with the car, and received high fives from the rest of our friends in the dorm. Everyone was sharing in my excitement. My journey to an aerospace career had officially begun as a sophomore in college.

About six months later I started my internship at Woodward where I was working in the Technology Development department. It sounded so cool, technology development, I was going to be on the front edge of design for the fuel control components. I had no idea what I would be doing or even what I was doing when I did get started. That is exactly what internships are for though, to gain industry experience and the skills required that are not taught in the classroom. I met my supervisor, Karl, on the first day and connected with him pretty well. I had gotten pretty into working out and Karl stood about 6'2" 225 lbs of dense muscle. I was just a string bean at this point standing at 6'4" and roughly 180 pounds and I did not appear to be a weightlifter just yet. Karl also wore glasses, had short blond hair, and always wore a short-sleeved collared shirt. He had a smile and look of energy about him most of the time. Even though Karl was my supervisor, I would be working with his team of technology developers, mainly Brad and John, on my day-to-day work.

I worked with actuators, pumps, electrohydraulic servovalves (EHSVs), hall sensors, and fuel valves. Some of the work in my first internship were menial tasks that required strong competence, but not in-depth engineering knowhow. After all, I was just a sophomore and early into my classes. I did things like digitizing PDFs of flow plots so that a digital database could be compiled and analyzed. I also proofread patent application documents. The times that I had my hands on some actual hardware components and was instructed to analyze their data is when I thought this was the good stuff, the "real" engineering.

One of my main tasks was to research the inconsistent failing of Hall sensors during thermal endurance cycles. A Hall sensor is a transducer that varies its output voltage in response to a magnetic field. It converts the physical magnetic field into an electric signal. They are used for positioning, switching, speed detecting, and current sensing. Thermal endurance cycles means placing the Hall sensors into a temperature oven and varying the temperature between the cold and hot conditions they would experience in flight. The oven was a large metal box with a microwave-type door on the front minus the viewing window. There were wires all over the place, a special hole was needed in the box for the wires to come out from the Hall Sensors and connect to the measuring computers. This hole was insulated tightly as to not cause much leakage from the oven during its operation.

The ovens were out back in a large test facility that had pipes running everywhere and test chambers lining the walls. There were large doors with small viewing windows into each room. The room with my oven was in the back right corner of the building and had a total of four ovens inside. When the ovens were on their hot cycle, the room would get a little toasty and I would sweat while I monitored the test. I was there occasionally to do a voltage test on the connector pins between the wires and the measuring computers. The Hall sensors were failing intermittently and we started to look at the connections as a possible cause. Checking the voltage difference across the pins would inform us of their connection strength. When the cold cycle occurred, the room would vastly decrease in temperature. Carbon dioxide was pumped into the oven to drop the temperature. Due to this, there were signs that read "If you feel lightheaded, leave this room immediately." If you spent too much time in that room, the oxygen levels would become too low. I do have to say there were a couple times that I felt strange, but never to the point of worry. I'm here to tell you about it!

I returned to Woodward the following summer for a second internship. They seemed to like me! This time I was placed in the Product Development department. Woodward wanted me to experience different aspects of the company and see the different states in the design process. Product Development could be the step after technology development. Once a technology is developed and initially produced, it could be turned over to optimize it. Another task of product development is to create new products using existing technology. I mostly worked in the latter with Fuel Metering Units (FMUs) and Fuel Metering Valves (FMVs).

I had two main tasks this time around. The first was a new project for a French aviation company in which a FMU was desired to be used as is, but the material and chemical processes needed to be investigated. The second one was a failing unit that I'll talk about in a bit. The United States and France have different regulations regarding the use of certain materials and chemical processes. There are some things banned in France that are not yet banned in the United States. If any materials and chemical processes fell under this condition, I needed to identify them and propose a potential solution. As I compared the banned substances list for each country, it seemed that France was light years ahead of the United States in terms of health and environmental awareness. Oh, and not knowing French and needing to translate technical terms was a fun time. That was a task all in itself! And another thing, comparing French and United States engineering documents was also fun with metric versus imperial units. The French documents were all in mm or cm and Woodward's were in inches. Permanently ingrained in my brain is the conversation that one inch equals 2.54 cm.

My other project was a surprise to literally everyone. There was a line of FMU's that was all of a sudden failing system gain and phase of frequency response tests. An investigation team sprung into action and I was one of them. Processes were looked at during assembly and test. Component dimensions were verified to see if a manufacturing defect had occurred. This started a few week string of 10–14 hour days. We needed to fix this problem to so we could ship these units to the customer. Another idea was that the springs were off which are used in the unit to compress the valves. I grabbed a bunch of these metal springs and tested their spring compression linearity; that is when they are compressed, do they compress straight or do they buckle/tilt a little. Before the test many thought this would be our answer, but unfortunately after testing numerous springs into the late hours of the night they all showed true.

I also tracked part lots and processes of all components throughout assembly to see if maybe a certain group of items was causing the issue. In the end, no matter where the parts came from, the problem was still present in the FMUs. I left to return to school before this investigation was fully closed out, but boy what an experience that was. We were able to improve the number of failures before I left, but not completely solve the problem. I was working so many hours, but getting paid overtime of course made me happy and I was able to get really deep into the weeds of the design to try and solve the problem.

NASA Radio Silence

WOODWARD WAS GREAT work experience, but I longed for something more. I was working on a component that went on a larger component. The larger component was bolted to an engine, and that engine went on an aircraft. Ultimately, the aircraft would fly a mission. I was a critical part of the process, however I desired to go on to a larger scale job, a "big picture" approach. Also, I ultimately wanted to get into the outer space sector of the industry. I wanted to design a plane or spacecraft, and even more so a mission itself. Now NASA, that's where my heart lied. I started to apply for NASA internships because, well, it's NASA and that was my ultimate dream.

I was using the OSSISOLAR website to apply for NASA internships. This website collected the 18 different NASA Directorates' and Centers' internship postings from around the country. OSSI stands for One Stop Shopping Initiative; it offers programs from high school students to graduate and post-doc students. Each applicant is only allowed to apply for 50 internships a year. I remember receiving the message "You have reached your maximum amount of applications." My thought process was 'You need to cast out as many lines as possible and see what you can catch!' But I wasn't just applying to every single one I saw, since there were over a thousand opportunities. I would take my time to sort through and apply to the ones that were in my field and seemed to align with my interests and desired skills. I filtered the search results to show me four selected areas of interest: *Aerospace Engineering, Mechanical Engineering, General Engineering,* and *Business Administration.*

As I was majoring in mechanical engineering, I was also minoring in business administration. The business minor was recommended to me by the benefactor of a scholarship I received. The benefactor was a member of the city and state legislation whom I had actually known for some time. He was a shorter man with slicked back jet black hair. He spoke with force and confidence. He complimented me on my ambition and aspirations of becoming an engineer and asked if I planned to minor in anything. I had not thought about it much and thought that maybe a math minor would come easily as I was going to be taking many math classes for my major. He recommended that I minor in business administration for it would help me out greatly for advancing my career and getting into management. That was a done deal. I did not question it once. I immediately planned to add a minor in business administration and it later turned out to be the reason I got my first NASA internship.

I applied to my selected 50 applications and hit submit with a smile. I took action and had excitement for what might come in the future. "How soon would I hear?" I wondered. One week went by... then a month... then six months. Unfortunately, there was just radio silence on the side of NASA. I received no emails, no phone calls, no feedback whatsoever. With summer approaching, Woodward had contacted me and offered a second summer internship. Woodward was quite impressed with the work I had done. Since I enjoyed my time there and had no prospects with NASA, I accepted the offer and headed back to aid in fuel control design in Rockford, IL once again.

After the first year of 50 applications and not hearing anything, I decided to up my game for the second year. I not only applied online through OSSISOLAR, I researched the position of each application via Google and tried to find someone at NASA who was in the department of the internship job posting. OSSISOLAR did not list any contact names or information. I figured if I could reach out to someone involved, they may be able to get me into contact with the right person and be impressed with my initiative. Therefore, I sent emails to people in the department saying I applied for the internship posting and wanted to express further interest. I added a line that said something like, "If you are not the correct contact for this position, I apologize and would appreciate if you forward it onto the appropriate individual." Once again there was radio silence on the side of NASA, I received no replies. Again with summer approaching, Woodward had contacted me and offered me my third summer internship. Woodward seemed to have taken quite a liking to me and it made me feel secure. I felt that if I wanted a full time job with them upon graduation, I would have no problem getting one. So with still no NASA prospects in sight, I returned to Rockford, IL once again.

After not hearing anything for the first two years and being 100 applications in, I decided to up my game one more step. I repeated the same process as the second year, but I also printed out and hand signed letters to send in the mail to the contacts I found. It occurred to me that email inboxes can be flooded with countless emails and my inquiry may be easily lost among the masses. I figured that not many people still use the paper mail system and that if they could literally hold my letter in their hand, I would definitely stick out. I printed out each letter on cream-colored resume paper and used professional cream-colored envelopes to look like I meant business, and I did! I sent those out over Christmas break from my parents' house in Kaukauna, WI. This was definitely going to get me something...it had to.

And it did! I received contact back from one person and was asked for a phone interview! The position was at Glenn Research Center in Ohio. The job was to test flames in a microgravity environment using their drop towers. Drop towers are kind of like the amusement ride the Giant Drop where for a small period of time they can simulate decreased gravity. This is in an effort to see how flames would react in an outer space environment, such as aboard the International Space Station (ISS). The ISS is orbiting the Earth 200 miles high every 90 minutes at 17,500 miles-per-hour. This research was to better plan and understand flames in case of their presence.

The interviewer was named Glen. We communicated via email to set up the call for a Wednesday afternoon. I was out of the dorms now and living in a two-story white house with a nice front porch right next to campus. I had my own room with a twin bed, small table with my tv on it, an old falling apart wooden desk where I did my homework, and mini dresser along the wall. As the scheduled time approached, I closed my door and placed a notebook and pen on my desk in front of me. The sun was shining bright through the window above my bed, lighting up the room to match my happy mood for this call.

The phone started to ring, I cleared my throat, swallowed, and answered with a smile "Hello this is Kevin." A friendly, soft voice that reminded me of one of my fun uncles replied "Hi Kevin, this is Glen from NASA. How are you doing this afternoon?" A pleasant tone and easy conversation followed. Glen described the work of the position in more detail and inquired about my class and lab experience at college. I was ecstatic to be talking to a NASA Engineer about possibly working for him! I was excited and sincere in my responses. I informed him that I did not have the exact computer skills that he had mentioned, but that I would take the initiative to teach myself those needed before arriving. There was some computer coding and programming required for the position, but I have not had any classes that taught those. I voiced my passion for NASA and that I would do whatever was necessary to prepare myself for the job ahead. Glen seemed pleased with my response and work ethic to prepare for the position. His voice was supportive and even a bit impressed I must say. He said that he would let me know in a couple weeks, probably through email whether I was to receive the position or not.

A couple weeks later sure enough Glen contacted me to inform me of his decision. My phone rang. I looked down at the screen and saw the caller ID from Ohio. I immediately got nervous, my eyes got wide and I hurried into my room from the living room and closed the door. I answered happily again "Hi this is Kevin." Glen replied "Hey Kevin, this is Glen from NASA again calling about the internship position we discussed a couple weeks ago." He went on to say that unfortunately I was not going to be offered the job and that they were going to re-hire the intern that did that work for them last year. My eyes went back to normal size, my heart sank a bit, and my shoulders sagged. I thought that this was going to be chance, my opportunity to work for NASA.

I was so hopeful and it seemed so promising from his reaction during our prior conversation. He said he felt the need to reach out personally though a phone call because he said they almost decided to hire me over someone who had already been experienced in the project. He wanted to tell me I did an amazing job during the interview and had great drive. Glen told me to not feel bad or disappointed or lose hope because I didn't get this job. He said that with my skills and dedication there is a NASA spot out there for me, I just I have to find it. The right one will come along, to not get discouraged and to keep applying and getting my name out there.

I was let down, but it was nice to hear the encouraging words. It was a great interview. I remember telling him about my *October Sky* motivation and then asking what his motivation was for wanting to work at NASA. He told me that he was an Ohio native and that an astronaut came to their high school to talk and that is what inspired him to want to work at NASA. This is actually a technique that I have learned is a great way to connect. I ask everyone I meet in the aerospace industry if they have a defining moment where they knew they wanted to work in aerospace. Most have great stories and I have learned to use this as a tool to connect on an emotional level with others. People get excited when they talk about their motivation. It shows them you have interest in them beyond just trying to get a paycheck, that you are curious, caring, and that you want to learn what drives others to do what they do.

I felt at this time that I was never going to work for NASA because this was my last summer for an internship before graduation. If I couldn't get an internship, then I wasn't going to have luck getting a full time job. I went back to Woodward for what I thought would be my final internship in the summer of 2012. I had applied to NASA through OSSISOLAR for three years, submitting 150 applications. I also found out that there were other NASA Directorate and Center specific internships that are not on OSSISOLAR, so I had applied to those as well. This put the total applications even higher than 150, but the exact number I am unsure of. After all of that effort, it seemed that my path was set to be living in Rockford, IL and working at Woodward after graduation. I did not feel comfortable with that. I had the drive, this passion deep inside me and I wasn't going to give up just yet. I needed to figure out another way to continue to pursue my dream.

5

Continue the Pursuit

HOW WOULD I continue to pursue my dream? Was it still possible? Should I graduate from Platteville, take a job with Woodward to gain experience and then apply to NASA later? Should I go on to graduate school? I never really thought about graduate school before. Honestly speaking, I did not want to go to school for that long. I mean, I was already going to be in the 17th grade after five years at Platteville. I wanted to become a real adult and make some real money to establish my life.

I was sitting on the front porch of my house in Platteville that I rented with seven other guys reading *Rocket Boys*. Summer was approaching, the sun was shining, the birds were chirping, and hundreds of students walked from class to class in front of me. We had the house closest to campus, literally right across the street. The street was lined with cars parked for school and the occasional tractor would actually pass by headed to its next job across town. A large old farm tractor painted your typical red, but it was flaky and mostly gone, rolled on by going to its next plot. Looking at that tractor I realized that if

I truly wanted a job with NASA, I most likely did not have the proper education. I was at a small agricultural school where almost everything we did was related to lawn tractors or farm equipment. Most of the student body was from the local rural farm towns where they went and worked on the weekends. In class I could smell the manure and diesel fuel soaked in their clothes from their time in the fields. Don't get me wrong, this stuff is important and makes our world operate, but it wasn't what fueled my passion.

I did feel that the Platteville education itself was spot on in terms of theory and a strong learning environment. The classes were small and you could talk to the actual professors instead of teaching assistants like the larger schools. However, I needed practical application and networking to my specific interests of outer space. This meant that graduate school was going to be necessary after all to further my education and acquire the appropriate skills.

My major in undergrad was mechanical engineering and I definitely needed more aerospace, specifically spacecraft, experience. I met with my Platteville academic advisor Dr. M to ask questions about graduate school to gain more information. Dr. M was a typical engineering professor with the standard slacks, blue colored shirt, and glasses every day. He was a patient and soft-spoken, brilliant engineer. He taught some of the most advanced classes that the college offered. Dr. M was friendly and taught concepts in a simple, yet intelligently complex manner.

I scheduled an appointment with him on a weekday afternoon. As I walked into his office on the ground floor, the sun shined through a giant window illuminating the place with natural light. I knocked on the door and he lifted his head up from the papers he was grading, "Hey Kevin come on in." I sat down on what looked like a 1950's metal school chair with a brown cushion, on the other side of his also 1950's-looking blue-green metal desk. "Dr. M, I think I want to go on to grad school to get a degree in aerospace engineering." His eyes opened up a bit more and a smile developed on his face. He looked as if he just discovered the answer to a difficult math problem or found out the correct process to use in an experiment. Dr. M took excitement with my desire to get an advanced degree and our conversation ensued.

He advised me to look at what research the schools were doing to gauge what I wanted to do. He educated me about the Graduate Record Exam or GRE that I would have to take to apply for admission—the GRE is the entrance exam for graduate school like the ACT for undergraduate. Choosing a graduate school was going to be a big deal of course. Dr. M said to me "Now you shouldn't only apply to the top 10 aerospace schools because they're flashy and go to the highest ranked one you get accepted into. Grad school is going to define your career, the area of work you would be spending the rest of your life in. You need to look deeper." He made sure to pass on his knowledge of choosing a school for its particular areas of research being conducted. He said "You can start out with the top ten schools, but then look deeply into them. Do they have projects and connections with the places you ultimately want to work? Do they have research projects in the areas that you are interested in? Figure out what style of research and sector of aerospace you want to ultimately end up in and choose your graduate school based upon those pieces of information." I now had some direction and set out to research what graduate school was appropriate for me and schedule my GRE test.

When searching for graduate schools, I did exactly what Dr. M advised. I did not just apply to the top ten schools and hope I got into one. I did start with the top ten aerospace graduate program schools in the country, but then I went a lot deeper than that. I found the professors at each of these universities and investigated to find what their areas of research were. I wanted to find the right advisor for me regardless of the school. Starting with the top ten schools was a safe bet to get an excellent education and be at a place that had "prestige" with its name. That alone was going to be tough, as well as figuring out how to get the advisor I wanted. I searched through tens of professors and their numerous research projects. I kept all my notes in a black spiral bound notebook and used a yellow highlighter to indicate which ones I really felt were cool.

I knew what I wanted to do in a general sense, but I did not know what it was technically called. I wanted to be at the front end of the design process, be one of the engineers searching for answers at the top level. I finally came across Georgia Tech and the two aerospace labs: the Space Systems Design Lab (SSDL) headed by Dr. Robert Braun and the Aerospace Systems Design Lab (ASDL) headed by Dr. Dimitri Mavris. As I read into the descriptions of each and their research projects, they were thrilling and right in line with what I wanted. I read phrases like "access to space, atmospheric entry and space systems engineering", "turn ideas into reality", and saw classes like spacecraft design and aircraft design. I knew right there, in the approaching summer of 2012, that Georgia Tech was the place to go. Space was obviously more appealing to me than aerospace so inevitably I wanted to work with Dr. Braun in the Space Systems Design Lab who was the leader in Entry, Descent, and Landing (EDL) technology research. Whatever it took, I was going to graduate from Georgia Tech with a master's in aerospace engineering.

In hindsight, I made a poor decision scheduling my GRE the Saturday after the last day of my internship with Woodward. I call this poor because I did not think about how much extra time and stress I would have at the end of my internship to wrap everything up since I would be leaving. This left me studying for the GRE with little time and focus. At the time, my work days were extending to 10 or 12 hours. I did study, but I did not feel as prepared as I could have been. I took the GRE on August 28th, 2012 at the University of Wisconsin-Oshkosh. I was on my way home from Rockford for a few days before going back to school and awaited the results. The GRE is scored in three sections: Verbal, Quantitative, and Analytical Writing. The results of my first GRE are as follows: Verbal 148 (36% percentile), Quantitative 155 (64% percentile), Analytical Writing 3.5 (30% percentile). There was another unexpected happening the final weeks of my internship leading up to this exam. An event that drastically changed my life had me moving to Virginia within the next couple weeks.

For this story we will have to rewind a few weeks to a day at Woodward. I was back for my third internship, this time in Production Engineering specifically working with Electrohydraulic Servo Valves (EHSV)—a type of valve to control fuel flow comprised of electronics & hydraulics. Production Engineering was about keeping the current production lines operating smoothly and also improving their processes. There was some cool aspects of this department, but I did not really enjoy working on designs that were 20–30 years old. I was fixing other people's problems from years ago and I wanted to be on the cutting edge of things. I was researching and testing flow path inertia of a jet pipe EHSV. I was using inertia tube theory to improve pressure and current stability with hot fuel tests. Essentially, I was adding little tubes inside the valve to restrict the flow path of the fuel creating a more stable flow. Hot fuel tests check to see that when the fuel's temperature is raised, the valve can fully perform. When the fuel gets heated during use, its characteristics change and alter the performance of the valve. So I added some tubes, heated the fuel, and then tested the valve in the chamber to see how it performed. This was a pretty decent task.

I also implemented a product engineering change to wire management techniques for one of the fuel valves. The epoxy that encapsulates the wires attaching to the connectors was cracking. I redesigned the epoxy encapsulation so that less of the epoxy was exposed and still met the design requirements. This reduced the number of times the component would crack and have to get repaired. In turn, saving Woodward a lot of time and money. I got some pretty good kudos for this one and left my mark, literally my name, on Woodward engineering design documentation.

Going through this internship I "knew" that Woodward was where I was going to end up if I didn't go on to graduate school.

Woodward was not a bad choice at all. I would be designing parts for jet engines and making good money. I would also be within a couple of hours drive from my family at home, and my friends. However, I desired more. With about three weeks left in my internship, I received a call one evening. I was sitting at my computer studying for the upcoming GRE. At the time, I was renting a room in the basement of house in Rockford owned by a coworker. I answered "Hello?" and hear "Hi, this is Kathy with NASA Langley Research Center." I responded, "Umm, sorry can you please repeat that?" Not believing what I had just heard. And she says "This is Kathy with NASA Langley Research Center. I'm calling to see if you are still interested in an internship." I was shocked, confused, happy, and anxious. I could not recall this job. I don't remember applying for a fall semester internship. I wondered how they got my application. This couldn't be real. I had to be dreaming.

Kathy had a soft and kind voice that reminded me of a loving aunt. She said that she was in the education office and was calling to inquire about my interest and availability for an internship. My heart started beating even faster than it had before, of course I was interested and I would make myself available no matter what! Kathy then said if I was still interested, the next day my "would be boss" would call me and tell me about the position. She also told me that it was for the fall semester, which meant that I would have to withdraw from my classes that were supposed to start in about four weeks, go on co-op, and move to Virginia. I said that I would figure out whatever I had to do and not let those details hinder me discussing the job with my potential boss. I attempted to remain professional in my response and not act like a kid in a candy store, but come on...this was NASA! I wholeheartedly expressed my interest to hear more about the position and work out the details with my school.

All of the next day I was constantly checking my phone to see if I missed the call. I was so anxious to feel my phone vibrate. When my phone finally rang, I was in the testing area where it is extremely loud. I was running a hot fuel test on an experimental design of an electrohydraulic servovalve (EHSV) I modified. The hot fuel test results were intermittently unstable and my job was to improve the stability. As I mentioned earlier, my task was to increase the inertia in the flow paths of the fuel. This can be done by either making the paths longer or decreasing the diameter. Decreasing the diameter was an easy modification to the design for testing with the insertion of a custom capillary tube. So after a month of design and fabrication, my valve was in the test chamber.

With NASA quite literally in my pocket, I looked up at the test technician I was working with and said, "I have to take this I'll be right back!" I grabbed a notebook and pen, and literally ran out of the testing area to get to a quiet hallway outside. My palms already sweaty and I was still wearing my lab coat and safety glasses. I anxiously answered the phone and heard "Hi this is Chuck with the NASA Langley Research Center." My heart started to beat faster once again. I propped my notebook up on the closest thing in sight, a stack of cardboard boxes, and started to take notes. He described the job to me and even said "It's the not greatest work, but we need to get it done. We will look for other opportunities while you're here to make your experience more enjoyable, but this is the main task you would be doing. Are you okay with that?" Literally, no matter what the job was, I was going to respond with "YES!"

Needless to say I was ecstatic! I could not wait to share my excitement with my family and friends. I did not want to, but I did have to finish out the work day. Happily, it was Friday and the weekend was ahead. I remember vividly this was a Friday because that weekend I was headed to Milwaukee to see my best friends. I finished up in the test chamber for the day and shared some excitement with my coworkers. They were the first to know, and then it was Dan, my roommate and best friend who lent me his car to interview for this Woodward job a few years back. I texted him first, "Dude I really hope I'm not dreaming right now." That definitely prompted a phone call when we both got off work. I drove back to the place I was renting to grab my stuff for the weekend and called Dan while I was standing in the driveway. The sun was shining bright as it was a beautiful warm August afternoon. "Dude oh my god, please tell me this is real" I said. "Super real buddy. What's going on?" Dan said. Just like a kid after Christmas telling his friends about his presents, I filled Dan in on the last 24 hours and that I was moving to Virginia in a couple weeks to work for NASA! He congratulated me and shared in my excitement. I was going to see him that evening, but I needed to share it with him right away. I was about to move 1,000 miles away for four months and took this opportunity without any hesitation. No thoughts of leaving behind my family and friends. This was my dream and I was going for it. I would tell my best friend Brandon upon my arrival, but now it was time to head on the road and call my family and fill them in on the great news!

I set off on the 94 highway. I was all too familiar with the 94 as almost every weekend I left Rockford and headed for Milwaukee—a drive of about 90 minutes that was pretty uneventful and 99% was just setting cruise control on the highway. Once I arrived, I trotted like a prize horse up to the entrance of the building, hopped up the three concrete steps, and waited for Brandon to come let me in. I stood outside the old glass door and when Brandon came down, he could see that I was beaming. Brandon is a tall slender guy standing at 6'2" with short blond hair. He holds an athletic soccer player build as he was also a captain on the high school soccer team with Dan and me. I had a smile ear-to-ear like a coat hanger was stuck in my mouth. Maybe I just won the lottery. He had no idea, but he knew something great had happened.

Adventures as a NASA Intern

THE JOB WAS essentially organizing file cabinets, sounds thrilling right? Well I approached it with a great attitude of getting to work for NASA and being able to hold the history of some of NASA's work in my hands. I also saw it as a foot in the door and an opportunity to network around while I was there and learn what was necessary to get a full time job. To pretty it up, I would tell people that I designed and implemented an organizational system for archiving and searching historic records of NASA's facility projects. I was so excited to be working at NASA I decided to start a blog to keep my family & friends up-to-date on what I was doing and to be able to share this experience with them.

The following are my blogs, raw and unedited just as they were posed on my WordPress site in the fall of 2012:

Adventurous Travels!!

I flew out of Milwaukee Saturday at 1:40 PM Central. I just happened to sit by the window right behind the emergency exit on the wing. There was not a seat in front of me so I had tons of leg room. I wasn't changing planes at all, it was just dropping people off. So I had this leg room the entire time! Just a great view too, took some nice pictures with a fancy new camera I got for a steal to document my adventures out here. I flew Southwest and the flight attendants were hilarious, they made the whole trip pretty amusing and enjoyable.

I was supposed to pit-stop in Baltimore and then head to Norfolk. Well there was some bad weather in Baltimore yesterday, so we got diverted to Pittsburgh. We landed and there was a plane at our gate so we had to wait 20 minutes for them to depart. Then we sat at the gate for about 40 minutes, refueled, and took back off toward Baltimore again. Once we made it there, we had to wait for another plane to land because we were switching pilots with it. When the other people started boarding I started talking to the guy next to me and the guy across the aisle heard us talking and became extremely interested in my NASA internship. Turns out he works for the NASA Wallops Flight Facility, we exchanged contact info. He did an internship with NASA out in California a few years back so he gave me a lot of good advice and information. I finally made it into Norfolk about 9:00 PM Eastern, jumped in a cab and headed up to Hampton in the pouring rain.

I am staying at the Suburban Extended Stay Hotel in Hampton. The start of my stay here is slightly comical. I was all set up and given room keys to Room 106 so I loaded up my luggage cart and headed that way. When I got to the room neither of the 2 key-cards worked. The light kept turning red and wouldn't unlock. So I headed back to the front desk with my issue. The attendant came to the room with me and used a fancy little device to plug into the door and unlock it. She opens the door and well…it's an already occupied room! She closes the door really quickly and walks away swiftly back to the front desk. She searches my information again and it has down 2 room numbers for me strangely enough. So I am actually in Room 142, when I went there it was all clean (well hotel clean, hah) and empty.

It's just 4 miles from NASA LaRC (Langley Research Center) right on the bus line. It takes about 40 minutes to ride the bus to get there unfortunately. So I rode the bus route today to get familiar with it. There was another little hiccup I encountered. On the bus route it goes into a loop on the Langley Air Force Base. So when we came up to the entrance the bus stopped and 2 people got off, I didn't think anything of it. Then a soldier came on-board and asked me and the other girl on the bus for our IDs. I pulled out my driver's license, as that is what I thought she meant. Well she meant military ID and I don't have one of those, even though I got asked multiple times while traveling if I was in the service. So it turns out I have to get off the bus and wait outside the gate while it makes it's 10 minute loop and then get back on, inconvenient. I'm hoping to find someone whose commute takes them by the hotel and we can carpool because it's fairly close and right on a major roadway towards NASA LaRC.

I start my first day tomorrow morning, Sept. 10. I meet my contact at "Badge & Pass" at 8:30, have orientation till 11:00 and then I get to meet my Mentor and figure out a lot more then. Feel free to share this with anyone you like and just let me know if anyone wants to be added or removed to the SENT list. I'll send you guys some more info later on in the week most likely.

First Day Escapade

Well I officially have 8 hours under my belt as a NASA employee, that's thrilling to say!

As my alarm goes off at 6:30 AM, there is no possible way I'm hitting the snooze on this one. Got dressed up all nice and fancy and hopped aboard the bus at 7:41 AM.

The bus trip was going all fine and dandy, gonna be getting to work a few minutes early, about 8:17 AM, which is perfect. Then the bus driver stops at the bus stop in from of McDonalds to let a couple people on. She then proceeds to exit the bus herself and go inside to get herself some breakfast....I'm not joking. Well she comes back about 10 minutes later and we continue on; according to the lady behind me this is a regular occurrence with this bus driver. So this makes me slightly late for work (about 8:35 AM), my HR contact calls me as I get off the bus wondering where I am. Once I told her, she was dumbfounded with my story.

She took me into "Badge and Pass" and got me all set to go with a temporary ID until I get my official one at my 2:00 appointment tomorrow. This means I don't have to get off the bus at the Langley Air Force Base now, Yay! I met a guy from Italy here on a 9 month work contract with NASA who has relatives in

Madison, WI and knew a bit about the Packers so we talked about the unfortunate loss to the 49ers yesterday. You'd assume I'd go right into orientation, but I did a little side help before. I helped my HR contact set-up a meeting room and got to meet some important men in the meeting discussing the education filtering program to NASA LaRC, the Langley Air Force Base, and the Navy. Next, I moved onto orientation and met another intern from Lincoln, Nebraska who is a biochemical major and in the Marine Corps. We watched the orientation video together and chatted a bit getting to know each other.

I finally got to meet my Mentor at lunch, and he bought me lunch too! He is the Chief Engineer of the Center Operations Directorate. He introduced me to the five guys in our department and a few others that were in the area where I sit. I share an office with another intern that is yet to arrive, or possibly be even selected yet. It was then explained to me that I was the FIRST choice for this position, it was just a frantic end to summer and a hectic decision making process by my Mentor. So that's a great feeling! Now I know that someone else didn't turn it down and I was an alternate, it was me the whole time. He also told me that my true boss is the President, hah cool.

I talked to the Standard Practice Engineer of Architecture, Structure, and Civil Engineering for two hours explaining to me some of the history of the department and what they exactly do. My primary job will be sorting through and organizing calculations of building plans from the 1940's to 2000 for the morning section of my workday. But then they are going to get me out of the office to see facilities, tests, and have personal interactions to gain important contacts and information.

They stated that it was a job that needed to get done, but they really want to get me out and make this an impressive learning experience. They really emphasized that at any point possible, they want to take me on field trips. It's some true "intern" work to get my foot in the door and gain the NASA brand value on my resume. There was a little talk about a summer opportunity, but nothing substantial or detailed.

I also will be attending some training sessions, lectures, and colloquiums to gain knowledge and information on the industry. I still have some more orientation and tours to do tomorrow, but that's it for now! Oh and I made my room a little more "home-y" by hanging a Red Tails poster on the wall.

Unforgettable Experiences on Day 2

Today was just a phenomenal day!

No morning bus issues so I'm off to a good start! I took the earliest bus possible, only 1 hour earlier with a different driver. I resumed orientation filling out paperwork and all the standard processes of disclosure agreements for confidentiality, patents, and media usage. Next the tour, time for an exhilarating experience!

First stop on the tour was the simulation facility. We entered the Lunar Landing Simulator and witness an automatic run of the simulation. During that it was explained to us what was happening and what exactly Neil Armstrong and Buzz Aldrin were seeing, computing, analyzing, and doing during their simulations. The set, the controls and user interface, and the atmosphere of the room was astonishing. After the automated *simulation was complete, the controller looks as us and asks "So, do you guys want to try??" I lit up! My eyes widened greater than they ever have before. We each took turns doing the simulation. Finally came my turn, I walked up to the controls and became a little nervous. I had to control the pitch, roll, yaw, and booster power of the lander to hit the target landing area. The simulation we used was the Apollo 15 landing site. As a joke when you land, you are actually right in front of a McDonald's on the moon, haha. So I got to run the Lunar Landing Simulator!!!!*

The next stop in that building was a motion simulator. That is, using 6 hydraulic lifts placed strategically on the bottom of a platform where a capsule will rest each operating simultaneously to "trick" the inner ear. They were doing work on the capsule portion, so we did not get to witness any tests unfortunately, but I asked if they would bring us in the next time they run a test and the controller was more than happy to do so. Yay!

Third stop in the simulator building was a commercial aircraft cockpit simulator. It was just 2 seats in a cockpit surrounded by large projector screens. There is no motion for this simulator, just the visual reference for landing and taking off to train and monitor pilots' reactions in unique situations. Unfortunately they had the Airbus (a French company) set-up using a joystick, instead of the American Boeing set-up using a steering tiller (kinda like a "wheel"). Still really interesting!

Finally one of the best facilities on Center, the National Transonic Facility (NTF)!! It is a wind tunnel using pressurized air and cryogenics. It is 30 feet in diameter with 2-in thick steel walls, and 500 feet long.

The models used to determine how air will flow around the article were mounted throughout the facility.

The technician was talking right up my alley with Computational Fluid Dynamics (CFD) and Finite Element Analysis (FEA) along with Reynolds Numbers and Mach Numbers. THIS is the facility that I dreamed of going in; a smile bigger than the sun was on my face the entire time. I was so anxious to see every part of this facility. The technician took us around and was extremely knowledgeable and informative about everything that we passed, he left no gaps in his information for questions, he was excellent. It ended with a liquid nitrogen demonstration of simple things like shrinking a balloon, throwing it on the floor, and even dousing Cheese-Its in it and eating them, giving a "smoking" effect through your nose and mouth as you chew.

I then took a quick lunch and was given some Work Orders to review because I was going to be taken out to the site to inspect what the Work Order was requesting. The requests were procedures for re-commissioning certain parts and devices in facilities to ensure safety and appropriate operation. Safety First at NASA Langley Research Center!! Always good!

Actual Work, Well Not Really :)

Ohhhhh just another day living the dream

Started out the day checking out our steam plant which contains 3 or 4 huge boilers, about 60 feet long and 10 feet in diameter. We are replacing one of the boilers and to do so we need to remove a wall. So I got to observe some discussions about planning and safety concerns between a civil and mechanical engineer. The mechanical found out I was mechanical and put me on the spot with some questions...CRUSHED THEM!! Good boost of confidence to swing into the late morning.

Next I actually started to do my hired-on job. I examined files, calculations, and drawings of buildings since the 1940's. I was looking at actual BLUE blueprints, aged-yellow paper, and pencil marks that were faded and worn with time to almost an impossible understanding. I came across the Electromagnet Scatter Lab (ESL), the Large Spacecraft Lab (LSL) [where they would actually test the shuttles!], and the Lunar Landing Research facility with the Lunar Landing Simulator that I mentioned yesterday along with a Mars Landing Simulation and Lunar Gravity Walk Simulator. Along with the Vehicle Antenna Test Facility and Space Radiation Effects Laboratory. These files included old photographs of the facilities and original artistic portrayals of what they were to look like. Some of the things I am going through hold true historic value and may actually be submitted to the Smithsonian if deemed sufficient. How rare would it be to say that I handled documents that went into the Smithsonian?!

After a while of that I sat in on a telecon meeting with Standard Process Engineers (SPE) from each NASA facility around the country, some of our contractors, and even the headquarters in Washington D.C. So I got to listen to discussions between SPEs of Kennedy Space Center, Johnson Space Center, Wallops Flight Facility, Ames Research Center, Goddard, Marshal, Jet Propulsion Lab (JPL), and a few more.

Soon after my alternate mentor, who I am actually working with, received a call and we got to go out and see some Lifting Devices and Equipment (LDE) that was shipped in from Kennedy Space Center. This equipment is being used to lift an instrument that will be going onto the ISS (International Space Station). We had to get a few things in order and checked out and I will be able to witness the lift tomorrow. I will be within like 50 feet or so of equipment that is actually going into space and attaching to the ISS!!!

Looking forward to tomorrow.

Reviewing History

Almost have 1 week in the books now!

Day started off with a meeting concerning the instrument to go onto the ISS I mentioned yesterday. Went through a procedure with safety guidelines to lift the $50 MILLION piece of equipment, ohh wow. Don't want to take a chance with anything that costs that much! So everything was laid out step-by-step like those essays you had to write in middle and high school about brushing your teeth or tying your shoe. That way if you followed what is written on the paper, you can complete the task successfully. Unfortunately it was not lifted while I was able to witness it, so I didn't get a chance to see it today but I will either tomorrow or next week.

After the meeting I went back to my regular scheduled programming, my file organization. I had so many pieces of NASA Langley Research Center history in my hands today. I came across so many facilities of great importance to everyday travel, weather patterns and predictions, and future technology. I kept tabs of most of facilities I reviewed today, the list is long and sounds intelligent, hah. Some are demolished, added on to, rehabbed, or still standing as is.

» *Aeroelastic Model Laboratory (contains a 16' and 19' wind tunnel)*

» *Transonic Dynamic Tunnel (TDT) (contains a 20" variable mach number, 6 and 8, wind tunnel)*

» *Gas Dynamics Laboratory (contains a 3" Helium wind tunnel)*

» *Hypersonic Aerothermal Dynamics Facility*

» *ScramJet Test Facility*

» *Supersonic Wind Tunnel (SWT)*

» *Aircraft Acoustics Wind Tunnel*

» *Systems Engineering Facility*

» *Aircraft Landing Dynamics Facility (ALDF)*

» *AirLab*

» *High Speed Hydrodynamics Facility*

» *Fatigue Research Lab*

» *Hot Gas Radiation Research Facility*

» *High Subsonic Acoustic Wind Tunnel*

Many of these facilities contained pictures documenting their building process. That way I got to see them almost built in-front of my eyes.

In between all this file reviewing, we had our first Co-op Luncheon. I met a few of the other students. There are four students from the University of Puerto Rico who have a slightly rough time with English. They are all in the Tool Design Department. There are two other ones that I met as well. I cannot specifically recall their departments, but they have both been doing co-ops at NASA LaRC for two or more years. We each stood up, said our name, our school, our mentor, and then described what our project was and its significance to the Center and NASA industry. There are some interesting projects out there for the more familiar and advanced co-ops. The co-op I met in my orientation with displayed interest in the Oceanic Air Show this weekend, so me and him are going to go to that and Virginia Beach this weekend. Gonna get out and experience what Virginia has to offer!!

*My Mentor gave me a book today, it's titled **INNOVATION IN FLIGHT**. He said he found an extra copy and thought that I would appreciate it. Oh boy was he right! It's filled with great information: statistics, graphs, tables of data, and pictures of course :)! Can't wait to start going through it!*

One Week Down!!

Well there we go, my first week as a NASA LaRC USRP student is in the books! [Undergraduate Student Research Program]

I started out the day by accompanying my alternate mentor, the civil Standard Process Engineer (SPE), to a construction site where a substation is going to go up. They were investigating the soil to see if the 140,000 lbs compact structure that continuously hums and vibrates would be stable. If not, we discussed ways to support or distribute the weight over a larger area than just the footprint of the substation. Some of the things we discussed were thickening the concrete slab beneath the substation, placing I-beams into the concrete to spread the load, or to put in piles (30–50 foot concrete beams drove vertically into the ground) in the area. A geotechnical contractor was there to assist in the soil support analysis. So I am getting a good variety of Civil Engineering experience and knowledge, which is pretty neat and I'm sure some of my roommates back in Platteville can appreciate that.

Then I went back to my building to get my picture taken by the COD (Center Operations Directorate) secretary. She creates a monthly forum for the department and they are putting in a section about me. It'll have my picture with a paragraph explaining my background and what I am doing for my USRP project. I will be included in the distribution of this forum and I'll post a copy on here once it comes out.

After that I continued on my file consolidation and organization. So far I am moving along quite well. I've eliminated 3 of the 11 file cabinets, so down to 8. Learned a lot more about the ALDF (Aircraft Landing Dynamics Facility). What it is, is a huge tank of pressurized water that opens a valve in a fraction of a section that shoots into a bucket. This bucket is connected to the back of a carriage on a 1/2 mile long runway. It immediately accelerates to approximately 240 knots and then slows to about 200 knots about 3/4 down the track. There are "rubberbands" stretched across the runway attached to barrels of liquid that spin when the bands are stretched. This is cause for a controlled stopping process instead of an immediate halt. The stopping forces and rate can be calculated from the time and turns of the barrels. The last time this test was run was about four years ago unfortunately so this is something I cannot witness. However, I did come across pictures of the test in progress and was able to flip through them like a "video" to see how it would look. It's very cool!!!

I bike home every day from work, about 4.5 miles. I go through the Langley Air Force Base to avoid some highway and today I had a Blackhawk fly over me and do some vertical landing, tail rotor pointed down, approaches. An intriguing sight! So then I got a workout in and then headed out to check out the Virginia Beach Boardwalk with the other USRP student. We walked all the way down the boardwalk, stopping to grab a burger and beer in the beginning, and then another drink later on. Taking in the sights of walking along with ocean and telling each other stories. It's mostly a touristy spot, so we are going to figure out where the local crowd is at and check that out as well. It was a good atmosphere to walk up and down the beach, a relaxing experience, just felt at ease. A good start to the weekend.

Starting Week 2

Ahh after a nice weekend of checking out the Virginia Beach Boardwalk Friday night, meeting some new people and going to a local bar (Brickhouse Tavern) Saturday night, swimming in the ocean at Buckroe Beach and enjoying a good dinner at the Green Turtle it's back to work today.

Today was a day full of going through the files and organizing them some more. I don't have too much info for ya today. I came across a High-Speed Towing Basing for Seaplane Floats, also known as the Seaplane Channel. It's kind of like the ALDF (Aircraft Landing Dynamics Facility) from an earlier post. It's a 1/2 mile channel used to test Seaplane floats and even torpedoes. I got to see some pictures of it, but not during any active tests unfortunately.

I started to make manifests of the file drawers to state specific information present for each building listed. This will make it easier to search for certain documents and also more convenient for my mentor to tell me what to discard of, archive, or keep recent. Just the life of an intern today.

I did have a good talk with my alternate mentor about some local sightseeing. He gave me tips on more beaches and interesting scenery to check out. We also talked about museums and other historical sites around the area. There is so much to see and do there. I plan on doing so much, but not sure if I'll be able to see it all. I'll definitely be going to Busch Gardens, D.C., Jamestown, Williamsburg, and the Virginia Air & Space Center to name a few.

I may not post everyday now, but if something interesting happens I'll be sure to put it up right away!

OUTSTANDING

Things are going great!

Yesterday I spent a lot of time in the file room, but then my mentor took me out for a personal tour of the ALDF (Aircraft

Landing Dynamics Facility). A little refresher on that from the post One Week Down!!

"It is a huge tank of pressurized water that opens a valve in a fraction of a second that shoots into a bucket. This bucket is connected to the back of a carriage on a 1/2 mile long runway. It immediately accelerates to approximately 240 knots and then slows to about 200 knots about 3/4 of the way down the track. There are "rubber bands" stretched across the runway attached to barrels of liquid that spin when the bands are stretched. This is cause for a controlled stopping process instead of an immediate halt."

He took me on the roads around the track and buildings explaining what everything was. He described the process of the test as we started out at the water tank and drove down the track giving me details of what I would see and what the instrumentation was overhead the track. We didn't go inside any of the facilities though. It was extremely beneficial to see the actual physical hardware of the pictures and reports I've been seeing the last few days.

Today was another day filled with filing, but had a few good things come about. We had a Center of Operations Directorate Forum where there was a little introduction of me to the entire department. I thought I would receive a copy of this to show you, but I haven't seen anything yet. After the meeting I was introduced to our department Director, she is one step below agency headquarters in Washington D.C. She enjoyed my enthusiasm for the industry and supported my project saying it was a valuable task to ensure our Center's future productions were efficient. This causes a great ease to the Center's budget.

After the meeting, I had an evaluation performed by my mentor. He graded me as OUTSTANDING and is extremely impressed with what I have done so far. I have been there for only 8 days and have performed my actual assigned job for about 4 days. It takes a lot for my mentor to be impressed, so I feel extremely honored. We had a great discussion about my initiatives to the project and the overall advancement of technology over the generations. We ended with a brief talk about me returning to NASA....they want me back!! After only 8 days, NASA is impressed and wants to keep me around!

I have been saying:

> **Give me an opportunity, I'll take it.**
> **Give me a challenge, I'll beat it.**
> **Give me an obstacle, I'll overcome it.**
> **Give me the chance, I'll succeed.**

for a long time, striving to make it a reality, show someone that I mean what I say. I can say that I am living up to my personal quotes. Today was a great day.

Future Looks Bright!!!

It's been a week since I've given an update, so here we go again!

Last Thursday, Sept 20th, I was given a personal tour of our 20″ Diameter Mach 6 Wind Tunnel and the Hypersonic Complex's Control Room. The 20″ Mach 6 Wind Tunnel has a model injector. That means that the model being tested is not originally in the wind tunnel. While the wind tunnel reaches equilibrium of appropriate temperatures and pressures, there is a device that shoots up and "injects" the model into the wind tunnel in half a second. Then the test is only ran for 7 seconds and the injector retreats back below the wind tunnel. I was able to see some of the models that they have and will soon be testing. Unfortunately the complex was shut down for annual maintenance, but will be back up and running next Tuesday. I was told to come and stop by sometime after that so I can witness a test.

The 20-Inch Mach 6 Tunnel in room D108, opened in 1958 as the 20-Inch Hypersonic Tunnel, is a conventional tunnel utilized for aerodynamic and aerothermodynamic tests of proposed aerospace vehicles, and for the exploration of basic fluid dynamic phenomena, including boundary layer laminar-to-turbulent transition. The tunnel uses dry air furnished by the facility and heated by an electric resistance heater, and it exhausts through an aftercooler into a vacuum sphere, to the atmosphere (assisted by an air ejector), or a combination of the two. Its diffuser includes a moveable second minimum. The tunnel delivers a speed of Mach 6, with stable flow in a core test area measuring 12-inches square in its 20- by 20-inch test section. Models can be fixed on the floor, or sting mounted on an injection mechanism, which allows a pitch setting from 55 degrees to -5 degrees and a yaw range of 0 to -10 degrees. Run times vary from 2 to 20 minutes, depending on the choice of exhaust.

"20-Inch Mach 6 Tunnel" The results of tests conducted in this tunnel are often compared to those from tests in the 31-Inch Mach 10 and 20-Inch Mach 6 CF4 tunnels to more fully assess the effects of compressibility and real-gas aerothermodynamics *under similar Reynolds number conditions. This tunnel performed a large number of tests during the Space Shuttle development program, and it is kept available during missions to investigate potential problems. The 20-Inch Mach 6 Tunnel is in service.*

The control room was a sight to see! The control room controls about four or so different wind tunnels. Each and every valve associated with the complex is opened or closed from this room. It looks like a giant video game, and that's exactly what the controller said to me. There are giant schematics posted with indicator lights showing exactly where everything is coming and going from. Again since the complex was in shut down, I was told to come back so I can see the guys in action.

Then on Tuesday, Sept 25th, all of the students working with NASA LaRC were required to attend a lecture. We observed a presentation given by the Advanced Materials & Processing Branch. It was interesting to hear some of the current projects being worked on and the story of how our presenter came to be at NASA. There are some really neat investigations going on into future materials and I can't wait to see some of them put to good use.

Then today I was taken on another personal tour of one of my most desired facilities, the TDT. The Transonic Dynamics Tunnel is located on Langley Air Force Base and is a closed circuit, continuous flow wind tunnel. The test area is a 16'x16' area so the test models are of substantial size. The medium used in this tunnel can be air or heavy gases such as R-134a or Freon-12. I was taken to the control room here as well and got to actually step foot inside the test area where a model was being prepared to be tested. The test will start next Wednesday. My mentor plans on taking me back in the later part of next week to stand in the control room and witness the test.

As for my future career opportunities, I have received another internship and full-time offer from Woodward, Inc. The company that I have interned with in Rockford, IL for the past 3 summers. Also, my mentor here at NASA has told me that he is getting all his "ducks in a row" to keep me on. He even mentioned the possibility of me staying on all year long; that is to say, stay working at NASA until September of next year and then go back to school. He said my next project would be much more involved into current and active projects. I have put in only 14 days at NASA and my mentor can't stop complimenting me, hah. Before he says something he says "Now I don't want your head to swell up anymore because I've made it big enough, but (insert compliment here)" Boosts the work ethic confidence every day!! Looks like I have a couple fantastic opportunities ahead of me to choose from. There is no complaining on my end, what I have worked so hard for, for so long is paying off. I am extremely grateful and thankful. Keeping it up!!

Truth, Lies, & O-Rings: Inside the Space Shuttle Challenger Disaster

Today I attended a Langley series colloquium titled "Truth, Lies, & O-Rings: Inside the Space Shuttle Challenger Disaster" by Allan J. McDonald. I learned a great deal about what went on the days leading up to and months after the incident.

The colloquium started out with the NASA control center video and narrator of the launch and explosion. It was a little eerie to watch, waiting and knowing what was going to happen.

The lecture started out by showing pictures and discussing how much ice was on the launchpad prior to launch. The root cause was a leak from a field joint on the right solid rocket booster. This leak is evident at T+.678 seconds(~Take-off plus..), but then disappears. It then reappears as T+59 seconds and at T+60 seconds it turns into a flame. The explosion occurs at T+76 seconds.

NASA originally stated that the crew died instantly, but upon further investigation that is not the case. One can see the crew cabin separate from the explosion and shoot off as debris. The back-up oxygen was activated, which must be done by the person sitting behind the pilot. Therefore, there was an attempt at survival, but it is believed they perished when they contacted the water.

There was a Presidential Commission to investigate the incident. It was very important to get the shuttle program back up and running. We were still in the Cold War with the Russians and the Shuttle carried spy satellites into space for us. That is why Reagan was quick to act in promoting the continuation of the shuttle program.

The launch was actually scheduled for Sunday, but was scrubbed due to a weatherman prediction. However, come Sunday the weather couldn't have been better; not a cloud in the sky. So the subsequent launch date, Monday, was issued. It took some time to get everything in order on Monday, and by then a front was moving in and once again the launch was scrubbed. The overnight forecast was said to be extremely low. There was initial thought that the o-rings would not seal correctly in the cold, possibly down to 18 deg F. The analysts said they would need predicted weather temperature at the launchpad for each hour up until the launch time to make an accurate calculation. There was a review meeting about the concerns of this issue with the Vice President of Engineering as the one who would make the final decision. He listened to the presentation and agreed that the launch should not go, but the quality personnel objected heavily to get the launch off. The VP recommended that they should not launch if the temperature reached below 53 deg F. The quality members were complaining that the concerns were not based on test data; that there was more substantial evidence needed.

Then there was a second meeting with some more substantial data backing the concerns. It was then said the temperature could not be isolated as the reason for the data of the o-rings degradation. Allan McDonald, the presenter, was the one who would not sign off on the launch. The other members of the review meeting then went above him to his boss and he would sign off on it. His boss signed the order and faxed it down to Cape Canaveral. While waiting for the fax, Allan attempted to persuade the members not to launch. Saying if anything were to go wrong, they would be at fault and he would be known as the one who tried to stop them. Well nobody listened and took action.

There were 3 big reasons that Allan McDonald stated were reasons why he would not launch. 1) O-ring concerns; 2) the retrieval ships for the solid rocket boosters were in survival mode with 30 foot swells heading into port; and 3) All of the ice around the launch pad creates debris and could affect multiple variables of the launch, even acoustics. The temp recorded at the field joint where the leak occurred was 9 deg F. The test takers said the calibration was off and corrected all the measured temperatures.

Later on after the explosion and some investigation, a memo was leaked to the New York Press about known field joint problems before the launch that have been going on for quite some time. This sparked an emergency meeting in Washington D.C. to get to the bottom of the entire situation of the explosion. Allan McDonald was part of the Failure Analysis Group and was required at the meeting. He testified at the meeting and the next day, he was removed from the Failure team and given a new job enticing him to quit. He thought about it strongly, but held strong and didn't go away. Eventually the people who heard his testimony found out he lost his position and demanded his company give it back. NASA even threatened his company with a termination of contract and a ban on all future contracts if he was not given a job of equal status. So he got his job back very quickly.

The Failure Analysis Group recreated the field joint and performed tests under two conditions: one at ambient temperature and one at cold temperature. The ambient temp showed no signs of leakage. The cold temp showed the same failure with leakage at T+.600 seconds. Thus showing temperature was a main component of the failure.

So the engineers correctly identified the problems. The engineers' concerns were ignored. The severity of the situation was not *realized and comprehended by the Mission Management Team (MMT) and the launch went on.*

It was a very interesting and informative presentation to attend. The other USRP student and I were most likely the only ones in there that were not alive during the incident, 1986. Learned a great deal though!

"Hanging out" with SpaceX & NASA

I happened to stumble upon some drawings marked CONFIDENTIAL the other day and low and behold they were from Wisconsin! Lorence Manufacturing Company in Newburg, WI did some work for NASA back in 1987. Pretty cool to see some stuff from back home that is incorporated into the NASA center.

I also attended a Government Technology Exhibit on the Langley Air Force Base. It was kind of half a college recruiting, half a software display. It wasn't really what I expected, but still interesting to see. Got a bunch of free pens though and a screwdriver/flashlight combo, haha.

Today I watched a live "Hangout" with SpaceX CEO Elon Musk and NASA Administrator Charlie Bolden. They discussed the launch this upcoming Sunday night of the Dragon supply capsule atop the Falcon 9 rocket. Its cargo is supplies and experiments for the ISS (International Space Station); this is not a manned mission. It will hopefully dock with the ISS within a day and then start transferring supplies and exchanging experiments. There are approximately 23 student experiments that are being sent up to the ISS, extremely noteworthy and impressive. Following this was a social media Q&A session. Some questions were: Why are we trying to send humans to the moon when we can do it right now with robots? Is there thought to discover resources on the moon or Mars and transport them back to Earth? and What is in the future for NASA & SpaceX?

We are not looking to transport resources back to Earth at the moment, but rather search for resources that we would be able to use there to enhance survivability on the Moon or Mars. Plus the transportation costs are too high for returning resources. They are planning for the first manned flight to be an orbital flight in about three years with then a trip to the ISS in four years. There is hope for a space tourism aspect in the future, of a goal to be about ten times the cost of air travel. Right now they are just in the beginning phase of developing the technology to make it possible.

NASA stated that they wish to "facilitate success of a viable commercial space industry." NASA wants to remain the anchor of the industry, but not the main cost. They are promoting a new form of propulsion research in quicker ways to do interplanetary travel. Solar-electric was mentioned. There is collaboration daily between NASA and SpaceX keeping communication constant in order to successfully make breakthroughs and accurately relay information.

Many interesting things are to come in the future! Communication enhancement is one of them that Charlie Bolden mentioned. I'm excited to see what this collaboration of NASA and SpaceX can produce.

Time for another exciting NASA tour!!

Took a break from the work yesterday to participate in another student tour of a couple of the NASA facilities. The two visited were what I consider the two most interesting and exciting facilities on center: the 8 Foot High Temperature Tunnel and the Impact Dynamics Facility.

The 8 Foot High Temperature Tunnel is a blowdown wind tunnel capable of achieving Mach 3, 4, and 7.5. The 8 foot is termed for the exit diameter of the nozzle. A blowdown tunnel is different from a closed circuit tunnel (where there is a fan that continually circulates the air around a closed circuit tunnel) in that it uses a field of vertical bottles containing high pressure air. The air is about 5000–6000 psi in each bottle and is fed to the tunnel using a 12-inch pipeline. The air is fed into a combustor and then passes through the test section area and continues out an exhaust end. The combustor consists of methane and air to heat the tunnel because with air at speeds of Mach 3, 4, & 7.5 and low pressures, the air temperature is unrealistically colder than what a test article would experience in real flight.

Something to consider is that to combust methane and air, the oxygen is burned. This is a problem when testing an engine that needs oxygen to burn in its own combustor. To solve this problem liquid oxygen is also injected into the combustor to create an oxygen rich environment. When the combustor reacts, it burns off the excess oxygen and leaves the appropriate amount of oxygen needed for a test engine. There is a tiny camera inside the combustor to visually record what is happening. This camera has a 1-inch ruby lens to withstand the conditions inside the combustor.

A couple other interesting facts of the tunnel is that the total temperature reached in the tunnel is between 2000–3000 deg F. Also the tunnel runs at a max time of 2 minutes, at that time all the air bottles will be drained and there is no more air to feed to the tunnel. There is an elevator to bring the test article into the tunnel flow area. After the tunnel reaches equilibrium of appropriate conditions, the elevator rises and the test article enters the flow stream. Before a run, nitrogen is blown through the tunnel as a cleaner because it is inert. During a Mach 7 test the air is running at about 1.5 miles per second at some points. Test articles include missiles and scram-jet engines. At the end of the tour we watched a video of a run testing a scram-jet engine, a pretty interesting sight. Unfortunately they will not be running another test until about the end of November.

Next stop was the Impact Dynamics Facility. It was originally a Lunar Landing Simulator to physically practice the last 150 feet of the landing. 25 astronauts trained here, obviously including Neil Armstrong. There were cables that held 5/6 the weight to simulate the 1/6 of Earth's gravity that is experienced on the moon. They would practice the landing at night. They had created a moon landscape and even created shadows similar to what is seen on lunar approach. The gantry as it is called, is 240-feet tall. The gantry has several antennas on the top of it. Antenna belong to the CIA, FBI, some TV stations, and of course our own NASA antennas.

We watched some videos of a couple tests that were performed. The first was a test on helicopter fuel tanks for the army. During a crash, how would the fuel tanks hold together? Would they break or leak and cause a chance for explosion? The final design was to insert a rubber bladder inside that looks like tire rubber and holds 200 gallons. They would not use real fuel in these tanks of course for testing, but instead dye colored water: green for the right tank, red for the left tank. Another test for crashing helicopters was deployable aircraft airbags that are just stacked honeycomb Kevlar sheets that would compress upon landing and absorb the shock.

Then we discussed the Orion capsule landing tests. The Orion capsule is currently being tested for landing in water, but it was originally planned to land in the desert in dirt and sand. It was originally said that it needed to be able to withstand a worst case scenario of hitting a mustang horse. It was then reduced to hitting a coyote and then down to hitting a dragonfly. They tested it with several different scenarios of deployable airbags on the bottom: sets of 3, 4, 5, or 6 bags. On the inside there are energy-absorbing struts on the platform that the astronauts are seated on.

Currently for the water landing testing, a Hydro-Impact Basin was built and will be active for about 10 years. It is not located under the gantry, but just off to the side so it has to be thrown into the pool. The pool is 20-ft deep with 3 slanted walls. The goal for the parachutes is to deploy and land the capsule at a 28-deg angle, but the tests go to the extreme of 47-deg to measure pressures and reactivity of the capsule components.

An interesting test was done for NASCAR actually. The test was accelerating a donated car from Richard Petty to 60 mph by dropping a 10,000 lb weight attached to the front of the car and wrapped around a pulley at the top and bottom of the gantry. It was then impacted into a slanted soft wall to measure the effects on the car and the driver.

At the end of the day I observed a teleconference on an update of the Mars Curiosity Rover with its soil analysis and discoveries. Some interesting finds and questions being discussed with more information to come in upcoming teleconferences.

The Role of NASA in the 21st Century— Dr. Robert Braun (Prof. Bobby Braun)

I attended a lecture as part of a four part lecture series for the NIA 10th Anniversary Lecture Series. (National Institute of Aerospace). This lecture was given by Dr. Robert D. Braun called "The Role of NASA in the 21st Century" who use to be the Chief Technologist here at NASA LaRC and is now a David and Andrew Lewis Professor of Space Technology at the Georgia Institute of Technology. He was also part of the first student group LARSS (Langley Aerospace Research Student Scholars) program. This program is similar to my USRP (Undergraduate Student Research Program) internship. The reason that this is so interesting to me is that I am looking to go onto graduate school to get a Masters in Aerospace Engineering and Georgia Tech was my choice. Not only Georgia Tech, but Prof. Bobby Braun was the #1 professor in the country that I wanted to work with. I searched for a graduate school program by finding research that the professors were doing that was particularly interesting to me. And searching over the last 6 months, Prof. Bobby Braun was the top candidate on that list for me. So I seized this opportunity to attend his lecture. I sent him an email the day before informing him that I would be in attendance and briefly describing my interest in him and asked to meet and talk with him after the lecture. He responded that he would gladly meet with me.

The lecture touched on all parts of NASA past and present. The Apollo program over 50 years ago was what defined rocket science. A bunch of 20-somethings defined what we call today rocket science. The Apollo rocket, the Saturn V, stood 36 stories tall and had engine for powerful than anything of the time. This all came from JFK's speech in 1961 entering us into the Space Race during the Cold War. Dr. Braun then states that he has a list of 9-Game Changing Civil Space Possibilities in which some have been achieved and are being improved upon. Some of these possibilities are: Predicting climate change, predicting Natural Disasters, Space-Based Energy, Asteroid Defense, Life elsewhere in the universe, Identifying other Earth-like worlds, Interstellar Robotics Exploration, Low Earth Orbit transportation, and Permanent human presence beyond low-earth orbit.

He then brought up a good question: What is the equivalent of our generation's "Space Race"? Many pondered what the answer may be, but there is no specific answer. Each individual has their own perception of what it may be. For Dr. Braun is seems to be exceeding LEO (Low-Earth Orbit) regularly and commercially and achieving human presence on Mars for surface exploration. Right now the MSL (Mars Science Lab) aka Curiosity rover is on Mars and weighs about 1 ton. In order to have a human mission, it is predicted that the weight of supplies and equipment would be somewhere between 40–100 tons. That weight is equivalent to 12 ISS's (International Space Stations) which would need 37

Saturn V rockets, the most powerful rockets we have, to launch. This obviously is unacceptable, so he went on to discuss the reasons to further other technologies that can be improved upon to reduce these requirements and then therefore create a more feasible mission. These advanced technologies do not only assist NASA, but all humans in everyday life.

Interestingly enough NASA was not originally for Human Exploration. When it was developed in 1958, it was as a combination of two things: 1) Science & Technology Agency, and 2) an Instrument of National Security Policy. Just to throw some budget information out there. In the 1960's during the Apollo program, NASA had 4.5% of the government budget, and from the 1960's to present the budget has been between 0.4 to 1.0% of the government budget. A substantial drop. Then when President Obama took office, he suggested a $6 Billion increase over 5 years to NASA. In Fiscal Year 2010, NASA's budget was $18.7 Billion and with the President's plan it would have put NASA at $21 Billion by Fiscal Year 2015. Unfortunately it did not go through, congress did not allocate the funds and it was an opportunity missed for the NASA program. He ended with stating the lack of public awareness of how involved NASA is in people's everyday life. All the technology people take for granted and don't know where it comes from. He mentioned that someone once told him that NASA didn't have anything to do with weather satellites anymore because he had The Weather Channel....where does the weather channel get its imagery and instrument information....not an intelligent statement. Ergo, the public awareness should be increased to inform people of the origins of their informational technology to show that NASA is productive and keeping America alive. I know that when I told some people I was coming out to work for NASA, I received a few responses of "Oh, that place still exists??" People assumed that since the Space Shuttle program was retired so was NASA because they believe that it was all that NASA did, a very unfortunate assumption.

So after the talk I stood in line and waited my turn to meet and talk to Prof. Braun. The first question I asked him was if there was a defining moment he can recall in which he decided to go into the aerospace industry. He told me that it was when he saw the Viking Lander land on Mars. And since all the work on the Viking was done here at Langley that is why he chose to come here. However, the work was all done, but he hoped that if they brought it back it would be here at Langley. They resurrected the program, but unfortunately the work was done at JPL (Jet Propulsion Laboratory). I then shared with him my October Sky story and he was interested by that and said it was a great movie. I then asked him if he had any upcoming activities at LaRC that I could possibly observe or possibly volunteer to help out with anything. He said he would have to do some thinking and look into it because he couldn't tell me offhand when the next activities were occurring at LaRC for his Georgia Tech research. He then told me to apply to the Georgia Tech Graduate program. So we'll have to wait and see if I am able to participate in anything the next two months out here relating to Prof. Braun's work.

Advanced Space Application Manufacturing!

It's been a while since my last post. There have been a few interesting things since then, but mostly grunt work.

I attended a lecture on "Aircraft and Space Based Applications of Advanced Materials" presented by the Advanced Materials and Processing Branch. The hot topic was Electron Beam Freeform Fabrication (EBF^3). It is a layer-additive process to build parts using CNC (Computer Numerical Control) techniques. That is creating a computer model and plugging that information into a machine to make a part instead of just "winging" it on your own. The machine will follow a computer design. The electron beam is like a laser, it melts metal wire that is feed onto a base plate or substrate. The metal wire is built up upon itself to create the part, one shape. This fabrication is done in a vacuum chamber that is 7'x9'x9'.

They are doing this to add features onto casting/forging parts instead of milling or machining features. It also reduces scrap and saves resources; it's a form of Green Manufacturing. This also allows for design changes later in the design process to be made more easily. It can also create unique shapes that standard practices are not capable of. All in all, it saves time and money.

The benefits of a space application are that tools or parts can be made on demand for replacements which is needed while in space. Also it could assist in building parts that are too large or too delicate to launch. To test how the EBF^3 would work in space, it was tested at Johnson Space Center on the C-9 aircraft, a.k.a. the Vomit Comet. It's a plane that flies in a parabola route to simulate zero gravity. It will fly 40 parabolas during its flight and each parabola will simulate 15 seconds of zero gravity.

More to come soon!!!

Vibration Testing

I was able to venture out and meet up with the SAGE III Team (Stratospheric Aerosol and Gas Experiment). It is an instrument that is going on the ISS (International Space Station) launching in August 2014 aboard SpaceX's Falcon 9 rocket, 618 days until launch! The purpose of this instrument is to study the ozone. SAGE III will measure the amount of ozone that has been lost and how much recovery has occurred since the policies on chemicals that deplete the ozone was put into effect.

The previous SAGE instruments were flying around on un-manned satellites taking measurements. Now with SAGE III being mounted to the ISS, it will maximize the scientific value due to the orbital path of the ISS.

To connect to the ISS, SAGE III will need a 90-deg attachment so that it faces the right way to see the Earth. It will use a NADIR Viewing Platform to do so.

The NADIR Viewing Platform is what I was able to witness being vibe tested. That is, they "shake" the structure at different rates to see how it responds and if it will hold-up. Simulating vibrations during launch and possible impacts from various objects are done in the vibration lab. It is vibrated back and forth in three directions, the x-axis, y-axis, and z-axis.

A certain frequency, or rate of vibration, is set and ran. The responses recorded set a baseline for the test. Then a random vibration sequence happens and response is recorded in forms of deflection (how much the structure "bends") and G's (how much force the object sees, 1 G = 1 force of gravity). Those results determine what the structure may see during flight and operation. Then the baseline conditions are set and ran again. These results are then compared against the first baseline results. If there is a discrepancy, it means something in the structure has altered or weakened and further analyses need to be conducted.

The test article is mounted onto the platform of the shaker. The shaker can be rotated to account for each axis.

As the test runs, it is hard to see the actual specific deflection of the structure. It appears to turn fuzzy as it vibrates back and forth, making it appear out of focus. There was a viewing window outside of the vibration room where I watched the test run in the X-axis direction. Right next to me was the Control Room filled with monitors and displays of each channel being recorded and video feeds of the test.

Usually a test is not that "exciting" to watch; you do not want it to be exciting because that means something is going wrong. However this test was kind of "exciting". There are eight bolts that hold on a particular part of the platform and two of them snapped off during the testing and it was immediately shut down. I was able to go inside the vibe chamber and investigate what had happened with one of the engineers. It was a very interesting experience!

Final Day

It makes me sad to say that today is my final day of my USRP internship with NASA LaRC. Even though some of the work was not too pleasant, I had a great and exciting time out here. I loved getting to say "I work for NASA Langley Research Center" when people ask me what I am doing out here. I also love promoting the MidWest saying I'm from Wisconsin. I actually ran into quite a few people who had close friends and relatives in Wisconsin, even met a few original Wisconsinites. There are some surprising questions I got asked out here: What are cheese curds? What is a Musky? Is Green Bay in Massachusetts? Is Green Bay in Canada? I have to say, well…some folks are interesting out here, haha.

I have been able to experience so much thanks to my colleagues and new friends. I have made some fantastic new friends and great contacts! I am definitely sad to leave them. Every day the F-22's are flying overhead, something I do not believe I could ever get sick of no matter how loud they are. I am going to extremely miss seeing them and feeling their roar. Also not looking forward to going back to weather full of snow and is 40–50 degrees colder, burrrrr. But I'm sure I'll receive a warm welcome from my family and friends.

I was required to write a final technical report about my work experience. I added in a section I called Interdisciplinary Experiences and would like to share it with you.

> *"Throughout my internship I have been exposed to an exclusive professional environment. With the high quality of people around me, I took this opportunity to gain advice and take tips whenever possible from my colleagues. I have witnessed not only engineering applications, but also business relations, budget concerns, operational procedures and processes, and several other aspects. My*

exposure to a diverse work environment has provided me with a well-rounded view on the situations. Not only have I been presented with business related activities, but some personal notes as well. My mentors and other colleagues were interested in who I was, where I came from and what I wanted to do in life. Having conversations with a personal touch gave insight into situations as I progress in life. My mentors and colleagues have become my friends and with that I have learned a great deal more about NASA and self-development."

The summer opportunities are widespread. I am currently attempting to shoot myself onto another NASA center to get some more hands-on involved research experience. I'm using the networking tools I've acquired and contacts to guide me down the right path. I'm exploring all options of NASA Centers and private industry companies to further my knowledge and gain real engineering experience. I am being nominated for a NASA Student Ambassador position as well. That would be an honor to have, to be able to inspire youngsters as I have been inspired. The reality is not only to be inspired, but to inspire others as well.

I start school back up again January 22nd and keep trucking towards that degree. I will be graduating in December of 2013 and am looking on to Graduate school after that to earn a Master's in Aerospace Engineering, possibly even a PhD if I see fit. I have not yet chosen a school, nor even applied. The universities are focused on fall 2013 applicants right now, but this does not mean I'm waiting around! I've been researching and exploring my options. First step is nailing the GRE (it's like the ACT for Grad school), and that'll be coming up in February.

Lots of roads lay ahead of me, several avenues I can take to achieve my desired success. My options are widespread and I appreciate each and every possibility and opportunity. Thank you to all of those have been following along! See you all soon!!

P.S. for my last day, I played Rocket Man by Elton John as I drove out of work.

Georgia Tech or Bust

I KNEW THAT my previous GRE results were not good enough to get me into Georgia Tech. I had to take it again if I wanted to achieve that goal. I was back at the University of Wisconsin-Platteville now not-enjoying the 20-deg F weather and two feet of snow on the ground. I set myself up well this time to take it early in my college spring semester where I would be able to prepare adequately. So on February 21st, 2013 I drove up to Madison, WI to retake the GRE. This time the results fared a little better: Verbal 155 (65% percentile) Quantitative 164 (90% percentile) Analytical Writing 4.0 (49% percentile). I felt a whole lot better with this score and decided to start my application.

Applying to Georgia Tech did seem a bit daunting to me, but I did not hesitate. Instead, I tried to figure out the best way to go about it. I thought back to Langley and my friend Eliot who was in graduate school at Georgia Tech. I reached out to him to see if he would be willing to aid me in my essay writing by reviewing my drafts. Through numerous edits and iterations of my application essays for Georgia Tech with the help of my friends and family (special thanks to Eliot, my brother, and my mom), I finally submitted my application for Georgia Tech and Dr. Braun's SSDL (Space Systems Design Lab) on May 8th, 2013. This same day I decided to email Dr. Braun informing him of my submitted application and that I hoped to work with him. I sent a follow up email just over a month later on June 18th, 2013.

On the same day of the follow up email, Dr. Braun responded that he will not be taking on students in the spring 2014 semester. I was pretty disappointed at this, but reached out to the ASDL's (Aerospace Systems Design Lab) space branch immediately after. I emailed the acting head of the Space & Defense branch in the ASDL about research positions. He pointed me to the head of the lab Dr. Dimitri Mavris, the ASDL director, for all research position inquiries. I was in the middle of an email conversation with him when I received an email from the Georgia Tech admissions office that really struck me down.

The all too familiar phrase "I regret to inform you that your request for admission to our graduate program has been declined." I sunk back in my chair, I didn't know what to do. I felt so disappointed and devastated. The only place I wanted to go to attend graduate school, had turned me down. I did not apply anywhere else and put all my effort and focus into Georgia Tech. However, within minutes of receiving that email and feeling hopeless, I changed gears. I became motivated to find out WHY and figure out what my weaknesses were so that I may improve.

My desire for feedback and improvement sparked a month long email exchange with the Professor and Associate Chair for Graduate Programs and Research, Dr. J. He informed me that he was traveling, so I decided to send two emails for each one of his emails back to me. My intent was to keep my name in his mind, show perseverance, and have my messages at the top of his inbox. The full and unedited email exchange is as follows:

SENT: June 28, 2013

Dear Mr. DeBruin:

I regret to inform you that your request for admission to our graduate program has been declined due to the limited number of slots in our program. Although you have a fine academic record, there have been many others with comparable and higher qualifications.

We appreciate your interest in joining Georgia Tech and wish you success in your career.

Sincerely,

Dr. J
Professor and Associate Chair
for Graduate Programs and Research

~

SENT: Friday, June 28, 2013 3:15:57 PM

Dr. J,

I have received your declined admission status email. I regret that I was unable to exceptionally qualify and gain admittance.

I believed that my commitment to education and multiple tours of aerospace internship work experience, as well as my strong passion for the industry, would grant me access into GA Tech's Aerospace Graduate program.

I was hoping I might be able follow-up with you and discuss the specific reasons for the declined status. I am interested in where the weak points in my application are. Would you please provide feedback on where I need to improve? I want to discover what it is I need to make myself a stronger candidate and be successful in the future.

I look forward to hearing back from you.

Thank You,

Kevin J DeBruin
University of Wisconsin: Platteville
Mechanical Engineering major
Business Administration minor

~

SENT: Tuesday, July 2, 2013 12:47:35 PM

Dr. J,

I am writing to follow up on an email I sent you last week Friday the 28th. I would like request you to provide me with elaborated feedback on my declined admission status. With a clear understanding of where I need to make improvements, I can take corrective action so that I may develop and represent myself as an exceptional candidate for future success.

Thank You,

Kevin J DeBruin

~

SENT: Tuesday, July 2, 2013 4:20:48 PM

Mr. DeBruin,

I am currently traveling overseas.

I will review your file and respond when I return to GT next week.

Sorry for the delay.

—Dr. J

~

SENT: Wednesday, July 3, 2013 7:54:53 AM

Dr. J,

Thank you for the reply. I will await your response. Travel Safe.

—Kevin

~

SENT: Wednesday, July 10, 2013 9:41:34 AM

Dr. J,

I just wanted to send you a reminder email as I believe you have several things to catch up upon your return.

Thank You,

—Kevin

~

SENT: Friday, July 12, 2013 1:07:39 PM

Dr. J,

I hope all went well with your travels. I am writing to follow-up on your email response stating that you would review my file and respond this week. I would like to ensure we continue to communicate so that I may receive appropriate feedback.

I still possess the will to know where my application showed weakness in accordance to the others with comparable and higher qualifications.

I look forward to hearing from you so that I may work on developing myself into a successful applicant.

Thank You,

—Kevin J DeBruin

∼

SENT: Friday, July 12, 2013 2:24:23 PM

the one day I was back in the office flew by—sorry

I'll get back to you when I return on Monday

—Dr. J

∼

SENT: Monday, July 15, 2013 3:55:48 PM

Dr. J,

This is just a reminder for you to review my application file. I believe it is vital that I maintain communication with you regarding this subject.

Looking forward to hearing from you.

Thank You,

—Kevin J DeBruin

~

SENT: Thursday, July 18, 2013 4:31:18 PM

Dr. J,

I hope all is well for you. Would it be possible for you to provide me with a status update regarding the review of my declined admission application to the Aerospace Engineering Graduate Program?

Regards,

—Kevin J DeBruin

~

SENT: Friday, July 19, 2013 3:11:35 PM

Mr DeBruin,

I apologize that it took so long to get back to you.

I have reviewed your file and here is the reason we were not able to admit you.

All our graduate students are involved in research—even non-thesis MS students. We must, therefore, identify a faculty member to act as an advisor before we can admit anyone. I was unable to do that because: 1. space design is our most popular research area and 2. your GPA is near the low end of the folks we admit. The fact that you indicated that you need funding made this even more difficult.

If you would be willing to work in one of the other design areas and were able to attend GT without funding from us we may be able to reconsider. However, I understand that this may be difficult and that you are likely to have made other commitments.

I am sorry not to have better news for you.

–Dr. J

SENT: Saturday, July 20, 2013 11:28:51 AM

Dr. J,

Thank you for the explanation. I predicted that my GPA would play a factor, especially in such a popular and academically competitive research area, but was hoping work experience, dedication, and industry passion would overcome that weakness.

I understand that funding is difficult to come by, as I have heard many times in the aerospace industry. I checked that box because I assumed that it meant was that I would be considered for financial aid such as Research Assisantships, fellowships, & other avenues; not directly completely funded by GA Tech. If I misunderstood that segment, I apologize. I just wish not to gain an incredible amount of debt if possible.

When you stated working in another design area, do you mean something completely outside of Space Systems Design and Optimization or just not Space Launch Vehicle and/or Exploration Vehicle Design? I am curious as to which other design areas are available. Could you please elaborate on those?

Thank you for the continued communication and assistance.

—Kevin J DeBruin

~

SENT: Thursday, July 25, 2013 3:55:23 AM

Dr. J,

I wanted to touch base regarding my last email. I requested that you elaborated on the other design areas that are open.

I also wish to ask you if it would be a beneficial move for me to apply now for the FALL 2014 semester for space design?

—Kevin J DeBruin

~

During this time I was not just waiting around to see what would happen with Georgia Tech. I started my applications for University of Texas-Austin and the University of Maryland for they had my secondary research interests. However, the main motivation in my mind, was to get accepted into one of these schools and then transfer to Georgia Tech. No matter what, I was going to accomplish my goal of graduating from Georgia Tech….by any means necessary.

What happened next I definitely did not expect. I received a call from Dr. J. I was sitting in my cubicle as an intern at Woodward on Friday, July 26th, 2013 working on a new vane pump design for the F-16 Fighting Falcon fighter jet. A little explanation of my work on jet engines quick before I dive into the call. Back in my fourth internship I was in Research & Development (now the renamed department for Technology Development). Typically gear pumps are used, but vane pumps are lighter, can be more efficient, flexible, and capable. Both types of pumps are positive displacement pumps delivering the same volume of fluid for each pumping cycle. In a gear pump, the gear turns moving the fuel around with its rotating teeth. In a vane pump, think of it as the teeth of a gear are free to float up and down in little slots as they rotate around. These vanes of "floating teeth" follow the path of a cam (the surrounding housing of the vanes) which is designed with a specific series of mathematical equations to give the geometry needed for appropriate fuel flow. At first glance the cam might just look like a metal donut ring, but the inner "circle" is a series of curves matched together to create the right position, velocity, acceleration, and jerk for the system.

In my work, I developed five vane pump calculator design tools in Excel concentrating on the acceleration or position curve of the cam. The five geometries of the curves were trapezoidal, modified trapezoidal, sinusoidal, cylindrical, and polynomial. These calculators would output the geometry needed for manufacturing the inner cam and gave a simulation of expected fuel flow performance. I researched and conducted behavioral studies for the vane pump platform. As part of this, I wrote and supervised test procedures, as well as lead investigations into our failed tests.

Now, back to the call. It's the day after I sent an email to Dr. J asking if I could already apply for the semester after the one I previously applied to. I stated this was in an effort to make sure there would be a spot available. My phone vibrated in my pocket just as it had from NASA Langley Research Center just about a year ago. I answered it. It was none other than Dr. J from Georgia Tech.

He said that he had heard my passion, saw my initiative to reach out asking for feedback, and witnessed firsthand through email my dedication and perseverance for Georgia Tech. Dr. J said "I've heard enough. I have created and opened up a spot for you in the aerospace program, but there is no funding involved with this so you will have to pay your own way." I was ecstatic, I could not believe that I HAD JUST BEEN ACCEPTED INTO GEORGIA TECH! I remember after I hung up, my eyes started to tear with joy & happiness. I was so elated, I felt lifted, like an out of body experience. HOLY CRAP I DID IT! I had all this joy and excitement, but no family or best friends nearby to celebrate with me at this very moment. I did, however, go and find my new friend and coworker Trace and tell him about it. He shared in my joy and congratulated me.

During the conversation Dr. J did however mention that I would need to be doing research as a requirement for grad school. He said that there was a new professor in the SSDL that may have room for a student and that I should also look into the ASDL, since it was a much larger lab. After this conversation I actually received a confirmation email that accepted myself into the School of Aerospace at Georgia Tech for fall 2013 as a mistake. I was immediately frightened. Did what just happen occur for the wrong semester and I wasn't actually accepted into Georgia Tech? I quickly called him back and he apologized for the mistake and confusion. Spring 2014 was the correct semester and I had nothing to worry about here. He corrected the issue and I received a new email stating that I was accepted for spring 2014.

I wanted to call my mom and dad right away to tell them, but my mom and my brother, Michael, were actually in Peru meeting my brother's birth family for the first time. My brother is adopted from Peru and we have kept in contact with his family. My mom hired someone to find out who & where they were so that she could share the good news of Michael's life in America. When my mom did return, I called her to share the good (and bad) news with her. When my mom answered I said, "Well good news and bad-ish news." She said "Hold-on, we'll talk on speakerphone so dad can hear too…Okay, what's up?" I said, "I received a call from Georgia Tech today. The good news: I now am accepted into Georgia Tech for the spring! Bad-ish news: it doesn't come with any funding, so you may have to take out a second mortgage on the house, but if you trust & believe in me I guarantee I'll make it and be able to pay you back." I believe she said something to the order of "Okay, let's not worry about that right now and celebrate you getting in!"

My Georgia Tech journey did not stop with acceptance though. I was still determined to try every avenue possible to get funding. I wanted to avoid the stress of going into debt and the financial strain I may place on my family. I first contacted the new professor in the SSDL, Dr. Brian, asking if he needed any research assistants. I did not receive a reply so I sent a follow-up email three weeks later. From this follow-up he replied and stated he had no funded projects with openings for research assistants. Well that was it, all the SSDL professors had replied with no availability. My dreams for the Space Systems Design Lab were at a dead end. I exhausted all possibilities for the SSDL.

At this time, I had honestly forgotten about Dr. Mavris and the ASDL (Aerospace Systems Design Lab) after I received my rejection letter. It wasn't until I was searching through my emails about a month later on August 25th, 2013. I then reached back out to him saying that I had now been accepted and inquired about a research position. I sent this email on a Sunday morning, not expecting a reply for maybe a few days. I was not in the habit of checking my email multiple times on a weekend day, but I decided to check and see if he replied. To my surprise, Dr. Mavris replied just ten minutes after I sent my email. He said that he would like to talk to me today or in the next couple days to discuss the possibility of funding. I replied as fast as I could with my availability and it was decided that we were to talk that Sunday evening. I felt so excited and nervous. In just a few hours, I was going to have what I believed to be a potential ~$80,000 conversation. Little did I know it was really a potential ~$150,000 conversation.

I spent the rest of the day researching the ASDL, refreshing myself on its current research and also the appropriate vocabulary that is used to describe the lab and its processes. Words and phrases like "innovative methods", "improve space systems", and "turn ideas into reality". All things that I found on the ASDL website, buzzwords that I felt would connect well with him. I also googled Dr. Dimitri Mavris to find a picture of who I would be talking to, to give a face with the name and make it feel like more of a personal conversation. Dr. Mavris had a stocky stature and an intelligent smile in his picture. He had his black hair combed over and wore thin glasses. He fit the image of a lab director, a powerful image of prestige.

I prepared notes to reference during the phone call as well as a copy of my resume & application to Georgia Tech handy to call upon if needed. I was so nervous, then the phone rang. I answered and heard an unexpected accent when he started talking. From his image it didn't occur to me that he would have an accent, but his name should have given that away. He had a soft spoken tone with an accent I have never heard before that turned out to be Greek. I was so nervous and felt very shaky in my voice whenever I was talking. I told him of my *October Sky* inspiration and what I ultimately wanted to do: "design space vehicles." He informed me of the lab's beginnings and current operations telling me how things work at the ASDL. Towards the end of our conversation I explicitly recall him saying two things. The first being "It seems like this would mean a lot to you." And I replied with "Yes sir, I would really, really appreciate it." The second being "I have called and talked to hundreds of students over the years to have this conversation and I am able to sort through who really wants it and who is just going along saying words." At this point I thought he was calling me out. I knew I was speaking shakily throughout our conversation so I thought he might think that I was trying to fake my way through because I didn't exert a strong confident voice. Then he finished it up saying "But I can tell you are really genuine and would really want this." A tremendous sigh of relief came across me, like a jury submitting an innocent verdict to the judge.

The next thing he said I could not believe. He said that he would like to offer me a Graduate Research Assistantship (GRA) and that would include my full tuition paid for and a stipend of $26,000 a year for my research work. I had to replay that to him to make sure I heard it correctly. I said "Let me get this right, a GRA pays for my tuition and on top of that I get paid $26,000 a year?" He reassured me that my statement was correct. I was shocked. I had no idea that I could get my full tuition paid for, yet alone get PAID on top of that. I thought the research position was either just work to do for experience without pay or a small wage to help out with tuition costs. I cannot recall what I said in this moment, but of course I gladly accepted and thanked him for the opportunity. He said he would start the paperwork. This was August 25th, but it wasn't until October 18th, 2013 that the official paperwork came through. A long time to wait for it to be 100% official.

After we hung up, I sat there for a few moments taking in what had just happened. I was speechless, expressionless. Sitting on the couch in awe of what I had just accomplished. Just a couple months earlier, I was rejected from Georgia Tech for a few reasons and now I was going to get paid to go to school there. Is this real life? I hoped I was not dreaming again! I flashed back to the moment NASA Langley called me and gave me my first NASA internship. It was real!

My mom and dad were headed up north to our family cottage on Arbutus Lake in Wisconsin. When I called them, they were at the famous ice cream stand stop in Cecil right next to Shawano Lake known as the Dairy Cove. It was about a two hour drive up to the cottage and the ice cream stand was just about halfway. It was a ritual started by my grandparents when they would bring my mom and all my aunts and uncles up to the cottage. It's a small rectangular drive-in with red shingled roof and baby blue painted walls. You order outside through a window, pick-up the same way, and could enjoy your treats on the picnic tables underneath their overhang. They even had special doggie ice cream cups so the pups could also enjoy the Dairy Cove.

My mom answered and said "Hold-on, your dad is outside picking up the ice cream. Wait for him to get back and we'll talk on speakerphone.....Okay, he's back. What's up?" When I told them, their reaction was that of extraordinary joy. They were ecstatic to hear the news! My dad even cried. He is not a man that displays vulnerability or sensitivity too often. They only times I have seen him cry is when he married my mother and when his grandfather passed away. This just showed how momentous of an achievement had just been accomplished. I could feel their smiles through the radio waves and cell towers. This was a miraculous moment that we all knew would help me on my path to NASA, eventually.

I called my brother Michael as well. I was going to see him the following weekend, but there was no way I could wait that long to tell him. He is an elementary school music teacher and was in his classroom setting it up for the start of the school year. His reaction was of the utmost excitement and he was extremely proud of me for what I had accomplished. We then planned to celebrate the next weekend with Rainforest Café because we were actually headed to Six Flags in Gurnee, IL.

Struggles as a Yellow Jacket

ON JANUARY 1ST, 2014 I loaded up my belongings in my mom's cherry red Chevy Impala and made the journey down to Atlanta, GA from Kaukauna, WI. My parents were going to fly down at the end of the week and were going to drive the car back home. It was about a 15-hour trek because of the snow storms around Chicago. The road trip itself was quite fun. I've driven it twice before down to Panama City Beach, FL for spring break with some friends. The worst part of the drive is Illinois because it's a long, boring state to drive through. Once I got past it, the scenery was much more enjoyable. My favorite part was driving through the mountains and then arriving into Atlanta at night. Driving in the city lights acting as a beacon screaming "Welcome Kevin to your next adventure!" I was all smiles trying to observe everything, but most importantly keep my eyes on the road and making sure I took the right exit. I was entering a city I have never been to before and didn't want to start out getting lost. I safely arrived at my new apartment, met my roommate, quickly brought my stuff inside, and fell fast asleep after the long day of traveling.

The end of the week came and my parents flew in. They were going to spend two nights and then take off in the morning of the third day. On the second day, we decided to go to the Georgia Aquarium. What a beautiful place! We have been to the Shedd Aquarium in Chicago multiple times, but the Georgia Aquarium blew the Shedd Aquarium of the water. It was magnificent. We spent the day taking pictures and my mom even talked her way into getting us a behind the scenes tour for free. We were taken up to the top of the gigantic tank and got to see it from above and learn how the operations were conducted. We were also able to see the poison dart frogs that were not on public display. Those were the most interesting to observe; bright neon colors. So beautiful, but so deadly.

The time came for them to depart, we had breakfast at the hotel my parents were staying at and then came back to my apartment. One of the saddest things I can remember is waving to my parents as they drove away. I did not know when I was going to see them again. I did not plan any flights or visits because I did not know how graduate school was going to be at the ASDL. Would I be working weekends on my research? Was this going to be a 7-day a week experience? I did not know.

I was part of a Grand Challenge team about Electronic Warfare. I exchanged some emails with the team leader, or project manager, while I was still at Platteville to try and get up to speed before I joined the team. A Grand Challenge at the ASDL was an open ended, relevant, realistic problem tackled by a team of graduate students while earning academic credit. They require a deep understanding of the problem's underlying theory and assumptions. As well as practical implementation of the advanced methods that are part of the ASDL core academic and research training (systems of systems and advanced design methods). Back in October, Dr. Mavris had one of his Teaching Assistants (TAs) send me a list of all of the Grand Challenges that were going on. They started in the fall semester in September, for I would have to join one when I arrived in January. I scanned through the list and found only two or three space related topics, so obviously I replied that I would like to be a part of one of those teams. I was told that those teams were already at capacity and was given a shortened list of teams that needed another member.

This was my first struggle to get my feet wet with a space research topic. Space was a high demand topic within the ASDL without much supply. A lucky few were able to select those topics where the rest of the lab did other aerospace or complex systems problems. I only really wanted to work on space, but it looked like I did not have much of a choice. Therefore I selected Electronic Warfare as my project.

Electronic Warfare was a project regarding protecting the Carrier Strike Group (CSG) against attack. The task was to investigate using unmanned air or surface vehicles (UAVs, USVs) as a front-line protector and/or reconnaissance device to alert the Carrier Strike Group as early as possible of an incoming threat. There were a few requirements handed down to us by the Office of Naval Research (ONR), but mostly it was open-ended. Our task to figure out the best way to go about the situation. We identified a plethora of potential UAVs and USVs that could be used. We took these vehicles and used them as inputs into a computer simulation we built of the Carrier

Strike Group and its potential environments around the world. We tested the vehicles using different flight patterns, number of vehicles, and several other parameters. We ran the computer simulation thousands of times and then had to sort through the data to determine which combination of inputs performed the best based on our evaluation criteria.

Our results of this Grand Challenge were to be presented at the end of the spring semester at an event known as EAB. It is where the ASDL's External Advisory Board (hence EAB) comes on campus for two days and the lab presents results of all of its projects for the year to our funding sources. Our Project Manager and another member of the team who was appointed Chief Engineer, were to present our findings. I was okay not to be presenting since I only joined the team halfway through the project and honestly, at the time, it was quite a fearful feeling to present in front of a room full of people who controlled the lab's funding. There were government and military officials, along with members of all the largest aerospace companies you can think of: NASA, Boeing, Airbus, the Navy, and the Air Force just to name a few.

The first few weeks of being in Atlanta alone were awesome, but also quite difficult. Atlanta was the first real big city I lived in. I loved exploring to just see what was around. Modern houses, old fashioned houses, parks, high rises, new restaurants, and architecture I've only seen on television were my new normal. There were skyscrapers you could see from wherever you were and several different neighborhoods, each with their own style and feel. I was living in Midtown, which was just east of Georgia Tech and north of downtown. It had a happy feel and things were kept decently tidy around the streets. It was filled with young couples, college students, and families. I moved into a two bedroom one bathroom apartment that couldn't have been more than 600 square feet with a biomedical engineering PhD student. My roommate was never really home, he was always in the lab working on his research. The entire apartment had old wood floors and the bathroom had a shower I could barely fit in. Our tiny living room was just used for storage of our extra belongings and bikes for commuting around the city.

When I first moved I only knew one person in the area, Eliot, whom I had met in Virginia because we were both working for NASA. He is the one who put me in contact with my roommate. I met up with Eliot a few times, but he was working towards his PhD in Aerospace and had a girlfriend. Needless to say his plate was plenty full all the time. I spent most of my free time doing extra studying to get myself up to speed on my projects, classes, and all things aerospace related. But also, of course going to the gym each day to keep my health and sanity strong. A break from the academics to clear my head, enjoy myself, and regain focus and clarity was essential for my success. Most of the students started in the fall semester, only about 10 of us started in the spring joining the ~200 students. I initially felt like an outsider to a solid group of friends that had been forged by going through the first semester of hell, I mean grad school, together.

All of my undergraduate work at University of Wisconsin-Platteville in mechanical engineering had been strongly theory based to give good depth of concept and the only real application taught involved agricultural situations. I took it upon myself whenever possible to steer my projects towards aerospace when I had the freedom, but it was never in a structured learning environment. I chose airplane parts or space vehicles whenever I had to do a project or experiment. For my CFD (computational fluid dynamics) project, I chose to do an aerodynamic analysis of the Naboo Starfighter from Star Wars. Yes I could have chosen a real airplane, but this was cool and I thought it would be good to know if it could actually fly or not. Most of the learning of aerospace terminology and specialty physics was of my own research through the internet and library. So as I am sitting in my classes and working on my homework and projects, I felt at quite a disadvantage compared to the other students who mostly had background in aerospace related things throughout all of undergrad. They were involved in aerospace research or had bachelor's degrees in aerospace engineering. I lacked the essential vocabulary and knowledge of basic principles that was assumed to be known about aerospace design coming into graduate school. I needed to catch up fast.

Dr. Mavris taught a few of my courses (Aircraft Design I and II, Advanced Design Methods) and his lectures were always three hours in duration. One of them was even on a Friday evening 3:00–6:00 pm. He would project slides on two large screens, one on each side of the room with a double wide whiteboard in the middle, and discuss the relevant concepts. The teaching assistants, or TAs, would post the slides just before class on the course website. I made sure that before every class I would download and print out the slides to follow along and take notes on. However, I think the main reason for this was to know was what coming. Dr. Mavris always called on people and even brought people down the front of our large 300+ person lecture hall (usually only ~100 people present though) to the whiteboard front and center to ask them questions. This scared the crap out of me for I knew I lacked the knowledge required to answer appropriately or sound knowledgeable in the aerospace realm. I always looked a few slides ahead every time so that I could anticipate what a potential answer may be, or get close enough to show I knew a little bit about what was being taught.

I really felt that I didn't belong, that I did not have the qualifications needed to be here. I was drinking from a firehose as they say every single lecture. I paid 100% attention, never took out my phone for texts or social media scrolling. I needed to acquire as much knowledge as possible as quick as possible. I quickly learned one trick to not getting called. If you were to sit right in front of him you were in his line of sight. So the trick was to be out of direct, frequent line sight. Out of sight out of mind, and also to pay attention. If he noticed you were distracted or not paying attention, he would call you out and bring you up to the front to go through the concepts. This showed he wanted all of his students to learn, to understand, and not just be there to pass the time. It was a good tactic that definitely kept me alert and on my toes.

My brother Michael came to visit in September during my third semester and sat in on part of one of my classes. He witnessed this first hand and got pretty nervous himself. He's like "What if I get called on? I have no idea what you guys are talking about?" I said, "Well I can try and help you haha." His plan was to stand up, say "Well sir, the answer is…" and then run out of the lecture hall as fast as possible. This did not end up happening, but I kind of wish it did! We had people who wore costumes to class and people who couldn't answer questions, but no one ever ran away in fear. Michael lasted about 90 minutes of the three hour lecture, I was quite impressed he stayed that long! He spent the rest of the class over in my office just hanging out. Yes, I had an office, but not a real office. It wasn't even a real cubicle. It was a room full of desks lined along the white brick walls that 20–30 graduate students worked in, each with our own computer and desk space.

Going back to the first semester and getting started at the ASDL, I also needed a sponsored research project to work on which is where my stipend would come from. This was on top of the Grand Challenge, so essentially it was two research projects and a handful of classes all on my plate. I went through the first few weeks without a research project for a couple reasons. First, the ASDL wanted us to go talk to the research engineers (REs) of the ASDL with the projects and see which ones interested us. And second, since I came to the ASDL in the spring semester, the orientation process was not as fluid as the fall semester. As I went and chatted with the research engineers about the projects, all of the space projects were already full of course since the projects started four months before my arrival. I kept talking to other research engineers looking for projects with an opening, and I was having a tough time finding one. This was actually an advantage for me because it gave me more time to work on my Grand Challenge and classes in the beginning as opposed to having another research project on my plate. Everything seemed to be full, but I kept searching and meeting with more research engineers. Finally Dr. Mavris found two projects that needed help and directed me and Steffan, another ASDLer without a research project, to go talk to the research engineers and see which projects we wanted.

Neither of the projects were space related. One was looking at processes to reduce FOD (foreign object damage) of FedEx operations and the other was something related to the Navy that I cannot specifically recall. Steffan chose the Navy project, and I was left with the FOD FedEx project. This did not sit well with me. I came to Georgia Tech to do Space Systems Design and so far I did not have a single task, class, or forecasted project in this area. I attempted to sign up for a Space Systems Design course, but due to me being in the ASDL I had to take the Aircraft Design course taught by Dr. Mavris. I took the FOD FedEx project, but decided that I would go talk to Dr. Mavris the next day. After one of our three-hour lectures, I went down to the front and waited my turn to talk to him. I wanted to be last because I did not want others to overhear my concerns while they waited to talk to him.

I approached Dr. Mavris quite nervously, my heart beating a little faster than normal. He seems like a god to me. He gave me my GRA and stipend, so I saw him as having tremendous power over my future and I did not want to upset him with my thoughts, but I went up and talked to him anyway. I needed to express my feelings and ask for a space research project. He listened intently, did not interrupt me, and even had a little smile like he was proud of me to come discuss this issue with him. I told him of my situation and my feelings and that I ultimately want to end up in the space industry. I stated that I did not think I was not on that path currently with the projects I had. He asked me which one I wanted and said that I wanted to be part of the Space Systems Mars Architecture research project with research engineer Dr. Stephen Edwards. He said, "Okay, go talk to Stephen and tell him I said it is okay for you to work with him." I was previously told that there was no room, but Dr. Mavris' word comes with some brass. What he says goes. Simple as that. No trying to keep me on FOD FedEx or redirect me elsewhere. I told him I was unhappy with my situation, told him what I wanted, and he gave it to me.

Wow, I could have been stuck doing something I didn't like because I was afraid to express my feelings and ask for a change. I learned that you never know the answer unless you ask; to never assume something is not possible and always give it a try. My journey to a NASA internship and acceptance into Georgia Tech should have taught me that I was now getting myself on the correct path for what I wanted to do.

The Space Systems Mars Architecture project was contracted through NASA Marshall Space Flight Center's Advanced Concept Office. Its research provided results of what a crewed mission to Mars would look like, the way the mission should be done, and with what vehicles. We focused on the outbound and return trip, ignoring the specific surface operations. We investigated what dates would be the most optimal to launch on, what types of propulsion systems to use, how to configure the vehicles, and what the estimated mass and cost would look like. In order to get to these results, our team developed an extensive computer simulation environment. We created it using Python as our formal text language and a program called ModelCenter that linked our analyses together.

We modeled numerous aspects of the work. I wrote computer code to calculate the mass of the habitats and also generated computer code to describe all the components we could choose from for the mission. We then ran thousands upon thousands of scenarios through the computer simulation, recording and analyzing the results. We would downselect the results using a program called JMP, which is great for large data analytics. To filter the results, we used requirements that we created with NASA Marshall. Once complete, we had created a recommended portfolio detailing our most promising results.

I also created a rapid geometry modeling tool for in-space vehicles. Simply put, I made cool computer models of spaceships. I did this using Vehicle Sketch Pad (VSP) and Python. This gave us a visual representation of the vehicles our computer simulation created. It was much easier to just see the vehicle than to read lines of computer code telling us what it was. NASA uses something called a bat-chart to display information about missions. It shows the top level details like how many launches, how many vehicles, what they look like, when will it happen, etc. I developed an automatic bat-chart generator in PowerPoint VBA (Visual Basic for Applications) to visualize mission architectures in a rapid, hands-off fashion.

I started to feel very alone in Atlanta. I've been alone before in Rockford for three months and in Virginia for four months, but this time would be for 16–24 months in Atlanta. I knew I would never be going back to Wisconsin because I was aiming for California after grad school. All I was doing was working and I did not make any super solid connections. All my close friends and family were 1,000 miles away. With all of this uncertainty and confusion I needed to write down my feelings:

I've lost my confidence, my optimism, my patience; my ability to be understanding, to forgive, to be patient, to be a source of motivation for others. I used to give others advice, provide a role model of enthusiasm, optimism, happiness, success, and all over great attitude. Where did it all go? I want it back, I NEED it back. It is my life source, my cornerstone, the rock upon which I step to achieve all the success that I have thus far. It's my base, my foundation….it is Kevin James DeBruin.

Now the task was to regain my focus on my studies and my goals. I recall a few specific conversations that made me do just that.

All of these conversations gave me the strength I needed to move forward and remember why I started this journey in the first place. While I was at my parent's place during spring break, I went to the local YMCA which is my home gym whenever I return to Wisconsin for a visit. I got in a workout with my buddy Josh McKenzie. We lifted and discussed my situation while he provided great insight and advice. He gave me an action that would superbly aide me in getting back to my normal self. He said "Go buy the book *Codependent No More*, grab a highlighter, get to reading, and mark that baby up. Approach it with an open mind, most of the stories are mostly related to alcoholism, but the principles are directly relatable. It helped me get through my time." I found a bookstore that following afternoon and bought it. I started to read it in the Milwaukee airport at the end of the week when I flew back to Atlanta. I felt kind of weird reading it in public, to have people see me reading that book. Reading the contents, however, helped me so much I didn't care who saw what I was reading. This book put a lot of things in perspective for me and directed me to be in charge of my own happiness.

After I returned to Georgia Tech, I had a phone call with my mom. I remember being very sad, confused, lost, and not knowing how or what to think. I mentioned something about not wanting to be in Atlanta anymore at Georgia Tech because the vision I had for my future and the work I was putting in was fading. She really put me in check. She said I had my vision of why I'm at Georgia Tech (my *October Sky* inspiration). She reminded me that my vision has been in the making since I was 10 years old and not to let something that happened just in the last few months deter me from doing what I was passionate about. That the feeling would be temporary and that my true desire would come through full throttle again once I was able to clear my head. She then mentioned something my grandma said. My grandma heard of my contemplation to give up my dream and said something to the order of "Is he an idiot?" She was spot on. She mirrored my mom's concerns and encouraged me to not let fear kill my original dreams. She said I would have immense regret if I dropped out of Georgia Tech to move back home and be around family and friends.

I wanted to be around loved ones since I was feeling afraid, lonely, and empty, but I was 1,000 miles away from anyone I truly cared about. Hearing that from my grandma was a terrific reality check. My grandma was calling me out! That was something I needed to hear and I love her so much for doing so.

9

Setting my Sights on NASA JPL

MY THIRD SEMESTER approached at the ASDL for the fall of 2014. During the first two semesters I learned of other lab mates working with NASA's Jet Propulsion Lab (known as JPL) and it became the only place I wanted to work at post ASDL. I knew I wanted to work with NASA when I started, but I did not have a specific NASA center or directorate in mind. Really, anything related to space travel with the prestigious NASA name behind it was fine by me. I just wanted to work for NASA and do space stuff, but when I heard about my lab mates experiences I was sold. NASA JPL specializes in robotic solar system exploration. This center is the one that sends probes throughout the solar system and lands rovers on Mars. These are really epic achievements!

JPL is located in Pasadena, CA just northeast of downtown Los Angeles. I never saw NASA JPL as a possibility when I entered graduate school. I knew of it, but it still seemed like an unattainable position. Even if I had a Master's in Aerospace Engineering, it felt like a stretch for me because I viewed it as the best of the best of the best. Only a very small fraction of people who desire to work there actually achieve that dream. I applied for some of their internship positions back during undergrad at Platteville. One of them was literally testing rovers in a giant sandbox they called the Mars Yard. That sounded incredible...and completely out of my league, but I applied anyway. Obviously nothing ever came of those applications back then, but their internships seemed to be the most interesting and exciting.

I was nervous I would not be able to land a job with NASA JPL, but I went forward and put all my focus into it. I had the mindset of JPL or bust. I had to pour my heart and soul into it to have any chance at all. I didn't concern myself too much with applying to other companies, even though I did throw a few applications out there, my heart wasn't in them. I went for broke. If I didn't achieve my goal, I had a Plan B. "Always be prepared" as my Eagle Scout status taught me. My backup plan was to reach out to Woodward, Inc. because they said they would always have a spot for me if I wanted it. I thought that was not a bad Plan B if Plan A didn't work. I would still be working in the aerospace industry, working on jet turbine engines. I was so determined to achieve my childhood dream, all my effort and focus was solely on NASA JPL.

Each year a range of new sponsored research projects are brought to the Georgia Tech ASDL. All the lab students get together and get to choose their desired project one-by-one. I learned that a project sponsored by JPL was one of them.

It had the name "Europa Clipper" and I had no idea what it was. I actually have never heard the word Europa before this moment, but I knew I wanted in with JPL. So let the Googling commence. I learned quickly that Europa was one of the 67 confirmed moons of Jupiter at the time and that it has the best potential for finding life in our solar system outside of Earth. Wow. And they were coming to Georgia Tech to have us do some research with them?! This was my chance to get a foot in the door. This was my chance to make some contacts and gain some experience.

I immediately reached out to Dr. Mavris about it. I said that I wanted to work on that project and that I wanted to be the project manager as well. I took the initiative. I did not wait until we discussed the projects in class with the other 70–100 students. If I wanted to ensure I was on this project, I had to make first contact. I crafted up my email to Dr. Mavris stating my desire to work there full time after graduation and that I wanted to be the project manager. He appreciated my initiative and enthusiasm which resulted in him saying that I would be one of the first to select which project I wanted. This meant the JPL project would be mine! As for project manager, that position is elected by the other team members, but Dr. Mavris enjoyed that I wanted the position and thought I would do well if elected.

The project selection day came and as promised, I was one of the first to choose. About six other students and I were granted early access for project selection since we were the ones that started in the spring and didn't get our pick of the draw last time around. The rest of the students were each handed a playing card and that determined the order selection. Those who drew Aces were first to choose, then Kings, Queens, and the way down to the lowly number two's. Let the selecting begin! Europa Clipper was mine and after me it filled up quickly maxing out at five team members total.

I did end up being elected project manager—goal accomplished. I felt quite out of my element though because it was about designing a spacecraft and I have never taken any spacecraft design courses. I had no idea what was going on honestly, and it felt like I was drinking information from a firehose and running while on fire.

I researched and read so much outside on my own time to try and gain the knowledge necessary to lead the team appropriately and make productive contributions to the project. I didn't even know the disciplines of spacecraft design, also known as subsystems: power, thermal, mechanical, propulsion, attitude determination, telecom, command and data handling, software. I was definitely not qualified in terms of knowledge, but I had the leadership skills and a strong desire to learn. I remember a lot of times taking notes with specific intent to Google terms later to really find out what they meant. I did not want to show my lack of knowledge at every step to the team. I was fearful they would question my leadership, so I made note of things I didn't know and then researched them as soon as I could. There is a time to ask questions and show initiative to understand and learn, but this was not an appropriate situation for that. I believe I learned more information in that first month than I ever had before. It was a true trial by fire experience.

The Europa Clipper project was to develop an End-to-End (E2E) mission environment employing a Model-Based Systems Engineering (MBSE) and Systems Modeling Language (SysML) approach to assess threats to design parameter margins for decision making support. Simply put, use some new design methods to create a simulation. We called our spacecraft JEB which stood for Jupiter-Europa Buzzer playing on Georgia Tech's Yellow Jacket buzzing and buzzing by Europa just like Clipper clips by Europa. It was a sanitized, simplified version of the Europa Clipper spacecraft. Our task involved creating reconfigurable Mathematica models and developing a modeling strategy for operations. Once we developed our models, we needed to combine our numerous tools. We integrated Mathematica, Python, GMAT (General Mission Analysis Tool), MagicDraw, MBSE Analysis Pak, and Analysis Server all together in our simulation environment. Basically we created a program where one could change an input and see how it affected everything else in the system from a mass, power, data, and cost perspective. Our project was evidence of MBSE's ability to give great insight into decisions for project leadership.

As project manager I was required to present our information to our JPL contacts and that scared the crap out of me. I am supposed to present information I did not really know to experts in that field. I spent every free hour reading and researching, setting up meetings with the team to discuss concepts and topics. I needed to become an expert in everything as of yesterday. I was already "late" and did what was necessary to acquire the knowledge.

One tactic I used was to have each team member review a PowerPoint slide I made that described their work in detail. I would meet with team members to go over their slides to make sure I was telling the right story. I was trying to convey their work through slides and to do that I needed to know what was going on. It was a great way to learn everything by attempting to describe it to someone else. Then when we met, I would question their assumptions, even if they were completely valid, because I truly didn't know either. I saw this as a great way to understand the fundamentals and theory behind concepts. There is also a book called *SMAD*, which stands for Space Mission Analysis and Design, which I pretty much read cover to cover, twice. This is a big whopping book of almost 1,000 pages and it was the crash course I needed. I learned by independent reading, trying to do the preliminary work myself, and then going over it with others.

About two months into our work, I was tasked to give our status updates to our JPL contacts via teleconferences. In addition to it being the part of the project manager's duties, one of our JPL mentors knew of my desire to work there and wanted to see me in action. Of course I was nervous about this, but I practiced until I was fluent in what I was saying. I rehearsed and rehearsed until it was ingrained in my mind. I wrote it down, repeated it in my head several times, and said it out loud multiple times as well. When it came time to play the game, I scored. The telecon presentations went very well. I received compliments from my other team members and the from the JPL contacts themselves who were pleased with our progress, my presentation, and my ability to field the questions they had.

The JPL Interview Process—Round 1

One day in early October I received an email saying that the Georgia Tech AIAA (American Institute for Aerospace and Aeronautics) student branch was holding a JPL resume critique session for the upcoming JPL interviews at Georgia Tech. This is where a few JPL employees who were Georgia Tech alumni would come out to Atlanta for a couple days to provide resume reviews to anyone interested in applying. I immediately signed up. The process for landing one of these JPL interviews at Georgia Tech was to first submit a resume online through the Georgia Tech Career page. The JPLers would sort through the resumes and then notify you if you were selected for an interview.

I went to the AIAA Event: JPL Resume Critique from 3–5pm one evening to make my resume attractive from a JPL point of view. There were four JPL employees at the event: two young women, a young man, and an older gentleman. All beamed smiling faces who were excited to see what their Alma Mater had to offer. I took time to meet with each one to get their opinion of my resume. I made a few changes, but for the most part each one said I had a solid resume. This made me feel pretty ecstatic and confident. I had JPL employees giving me compliments! I felt pretty comfortable submitting my resume to the online page and then waited to hear back.

A couple weeks later on October 19th, 2014 which was a Sunday night, I was in Huntsville, AL. I was at NASA's Marshall Space Flight Center with my team to present the results of our Space Systems Mars Architecture project. We were in our hotel room reviewing and finalizing the presentation for tomorrow when I received an email. The email subject line was "JPL On-Campus Interview" and started off with "Congratulations! You have been selected..." stating that I was going to be talking to two JPL recruiters for an hour when they come into town in late October. Just seeing that subject line made my heart jump. I was so excited inside, but kept my composure around my fellow researchers. We had an important meeting tomorrow that we were all working feverishly to be prepared for through the late hours of the night. I immediately screenshotted the email on my phone and sent that picture to my friends and family so that they could share in my happiness and excitement. I received a bunch of "Congrats!" and "You're gonna kill it!" from everyone. I had the support of my close friends & family which helped drive me to success. I delved in the great excitement secretly among my fellow researches. I did inform them of the email and they said "Nice!", but I did not want to get all giddy & joyous in front of them as we prepped for a big day ahead of us. I smiled a lot, but had to be focused on the task at hand.

The next day, our research presentations went smoothly and NASA Marshall was pleased with what we had done. I can't disclose the exact details of course, but our research was to provide results of what a crewed mission to Mars would look like in terms of architecture. Architecture is the way the mission could be done and with what vehicles. We focused on the outbound and return trip, ignoring the specific surface operations. We presented what dates would be the most optimal to launch on, what types of propulsion systems to use, how to configure the vehicles, and what the estimated mass and cost would look like. To get to these results, our research work was building up a massive computer simulation environment to model numerous aspects of the work and ran thousands upon thousands of scenarios through the environment recording and analyzing the results.

The JPL Interview Process—Round 2

The Georgia Tech JPL interview was fast approaching and I put myself into prep mode immediately upon return from NASA Marshall. I've made it to the second round, past the first round of an online resume submission and review. For this interview, I did what I do best: researched what I needed to know to be successful. I was applying for a Systems Engineering position. Systems engineers are responsible for integrating the design to make sure everything comes together properly within the constraints of the design. They are a jack-of-all-trades in the aerospace realm making sure this complex puzzle fits together nicely. A system engineer needs to know how the low level decisions can ripple through the design and how they affect the high level big picture items.

I searched for systems engineering papers about JPL or authored by a JPL employee. This helped me get the vocabulary that the JPLers would be familiar with so we could converse smoothly and they would see me as a good fit. I found two papers specifically that I still have on my computer today. One of them was titled, "Advancing the Practice of Systems Engineering at JPL" by P.A. "Trisha" Jansma and Ross M. Jones. This paper was about how JPL improves its systems engineers by certain training methods.

The other paper was "If You Want Good System Engineers, Sometimes You Have To Grow Your Own!" by, again, P.A. "Trisha" Jansma and Mary Ellen Derro. The title of this paper gave me hope in that JPL has published that they like to train systems engineers themselves. I could be one of those that they build up and trained specifically for what they want, since I was not "corrupted" by industry by coming right out of school. This also meant to me that I did not have to have the exact credentials that were needed right out of school. If I showed a strong potential and ability to be coached, I could land the job and JPL would bring me up the rest of the way to gain the appropriate experience.

I highlighted some specific parts of this paper that stood out to me matching my skills and showed me I was meant to be a systems engineer. It stated that good systems engineers have four main behavioral attributes: leadership, communication, 'problem solving and systems thinking', and 'attitudes and attributes'. I believe, and have been told by others, that I possess these characteristics and it gave me a strong sense that I was going for the right career. Two additional phrases stood out to me. They described what systems engineering is and what a good systems engineer does.

> "They have the ability to view the big picture, zoom in to pinpoint the "disconnect", and then zoom back out to the big picture, while at the same time looking at the interrelationships and patterns in the system design. They have a high degree of curiosity mixed with self-confidence and persistence and are achievement-oriented."

"They are drawn to the challenge of solving complex problems and are creative in the midst of numerous constraints."

Hopefully that gives you an idea of the responsibilities of a systems engineer. We essentially are responsible for integrating the design, needing to know the small technical details and how they relate to everything else in the design to make it come together and function properly. I was always focused on the big picture on every project I was involved in. Being a systems engineer seemed to be a natural tendency for me. One more thing I took from this paper was two sample interview questions that were stated. 1) "Tell us one of the most difficult problems you had to solve. What was it and how did you go about solving it?" 2) "Tell us a time when you had to build a consensus with different team members. Step us through how you did it." And I actually did receive very similar questions during my interview.

The JPL recruiter sent out an email notifying everyone of their interview times. The strange thing here was that he sent a link to a PDF that listed everyone's name that was interviewing, who they would be interviewing with, and at what times. I'm not sure if this was one of JPL's tactics in interviewing/ recruiting, but the document revealed each candidate that would be interviewing to give off the idea that they are not the only one. Maybe a way to incite stronger competition or something, not quite sure. I found out years later that it was a mistake. Anyway, I saw my time and that I would be chatting with two JPLers. I was so excited and nervous.

I put on my suit and tie and headed to the interview. I remember stopping to take a selfie with Georgia Tech's Tech Tower in the background. It is a large clock tower with 'TECH' lit up at night on all four sides. I did this as a memory, to capture my smile, excitement, and nervousness as my current position as a Georgia Tech GRA hoping to become a NASA JPL systems engineer. I walked into the building and my hands were already sweating. I placed my hands in my pockets, squeezed the Kleenexes and dried my hands. You don't want a sweaty handshake! I went down the elevator and walked into a large room where the recruiter was sitting at a table with his computer. I went up, introduced myself and he said to have a seat, the interviewers were finishing up with another candidate and would be with me shortly. There was another individual waiting with me whom I decided to strike up a conversation with to pass that time. Little did I know, this individual would be my intern in the future, and I wouldn't even remember meeting him here when I aided in hiring him.

Now the interview. I was escorted to a small room, no bigger than six by ten feet. Here the two JPLers sat behind a table. I unbuttoned my suit coat, flipped it open, and sat down ready to chat with a smile. We each introduced ourselves. I had my portfolio in front of me in which I took notes. I made sure to write down both of their names at the top of the page, so if I had a lapse in my memory when chatting, I could look down and quickly remember the names of the seemingly intimidating JPLers. On this paper I also came geared up with a list of questions I had prepared beforehand. An inquisitive and curious individual is a good sign of a strong candidate. An individual that is interested to learn more and ask intelligent questions is something that I've learned recruiters and interviewers look for in an individual with potential.

An interview question that sticks out in my mind was when I was asked about some Matlab coding experience for determining optimization of a UAV (unmanned aerial vehicle) surveillance flight pattern. Matlab is a computer coding language in which you can write mathematical equations and logical functions to generate a computer simulation and perform analyses. This was not my strong suit, but I was learning as I went. I told them that I did not know Matlab before coming to graduate school only nine months ago, but that I had just coded up a genetic algorithm to perform my optimization problem. One of the interviewers seemed quite impressed and asked me to describe in detail how I coded the algorithm. Internally I was extremely terrified because I could not fake my way through it, he would know. But of course I said sure and started to describe what I could recall.

If you do not know what a genetic algorithm is, it is a way to generate a series of input variables or "create a population" to run through the simulation. Then you take members of the population and pin them against each other in a tournament style fashion. This means taking the results of two different simulations, comparing them against each other to see which one is closer to your desired outcome. The winners go on, and the losers fall out. Once you have a set of winners, you actually tweak them slightly to form a new population and run them against the original winners. This process is repeated until one is seen as ultimately victorious, or if an end-criteria you've established is reached. This is essentially what I told him, but with a few more code details such as bit-flipping to make adults multiply children and probability generation for victory determination. I talked about binary code and gray code as well as my objective function for comparison and ultimate victory. He seemed satisfied with my answer.

One of the main components of the interview was the JPLers trying to figure out what I wanted to do at JPL. They mentioned there are many different aspects that go into designing a spacecraft and different phases in its lifecycle. They stated that they were trying to figure out which departments to give my resume to for further consideration. This made me feel pretty great because they were already talking about showing my resume to more people for the next step! One of the things I believed strongly helped me was name-dropping my two JPL contacts from my research project and having that research project on my resume. Having a JPL project and stating I was working with two JPLers came off strong and impressive. I did not know it at the time, but the names of the JPLers I dropped actually carried a good amount of weight behind them. They are extremely well respected members of the JPL community.

We concluded the interview, stood up, shook one another's hands, and exchanged business cards. I walked out of the interview feeling confident and happy with my performance. I would now be in the waiting game to hear back from them if I was to continue on in the interview process. They said it would be three to five weeks until I would receive word if I was moving on or not, but either way I should get notified. I have never just played the waiting game, as history has shown I have always continued to follow-up in the meantime. Quite quickly after the interview, maybe a couple days, I sent a thank you email to my two interviewers. When the three week mark occurred, I sent another email following up to reiterate my interest and a short summary of my skills we discussed with my resume attached again for quick reference.

Later that week, the phone in my pocket vibrated while I was working in the lab. I pulled it out and saw Los Angeles stated on the caller ID. My heart jumped and I jumped up to head out of the lab to take the call. It was JPL of course, someone in Division 39 Flight Operations was calling to invite me to come out for an interview and to set up travel arrangements. I was ecstatic, I made it to the next round! I was told it was to be a full day of interviews and a one hour presentation to a panel describing my work in more detail. I was given two options for my interview: the week of finals or the week after. Those were the times JPL had available, so I obviously picked the week after finals to avoid conflict. I tried to be smart about the travel arrangements since they were going to be paying for it. The interview was scheduled for December 18th, 2014. Since this was right before Christmas break at Georgia Tech I decided to see if I could get JPL to fly me back to Wisconsin from California instead of back to Atlanta. It took a few days to sort out, but since my home & permanent address was listed as Wisconsin they were able to fly me back home. Sweet! I just saved $200 on a flight back home…score.

The next week I received another call from JPL, this time from Division 31 Project Systems Engineering & Formulation. They also wanted to fly me out for an interview. I told them I was already contacted by Division 39 and I would be out there on

December 18th. I found it surprising that the divisions didn't know about each other's desire to fly me out. I figured it all came through the HR office, but I guess not. Each division takes control of their own interviews. So Division 31 said it would work together with Division 39 and coordinate my interview together. This had me feeling exceptionally well. Not one, but TWO divisions had deemed me worthy for an on-site interview at JPL. It seemed that I was well on my way to getting a full time job at JPL.

Round 3 of JPL Interviews

WITH A TRIP to NASA JPL approaching quickly, preparation for the on-site interview began with making my presentation. I was told that I would have one hour to present my work. To show technical details and to also show who I am outside of my career. This meant creating PowerPoint slides that I would talk through for about 40 minutes. The presentation slot was allocated for 60 minutes, but JPL is known for asking many questions throughout. It is also good practice to have margin and leave room at the end for questions. One of the worst things you can do is to not finish your slides. It shows that you didn't prepare appropriately and if part of it is due to questions and talking in the room, it means you did not lead and control the room well enough. Not the kind of impression you want to leave in a job interview. I buckled down and got to work.

I sat down and compiled my graduate work as well as my Woodward internship projects. Woodward was my only real hands-on technical experience and I needed to showcase that.

First though, I stated I was from Kaukauna, WI and an active individual loving all things fitness. I also showcased my Eagle Scout project about building a 30-foot walkway and 30-foot diameter brick patio fire pit for a handicapped hunting facility. I went in chronological order starting with the Woodward internships, going more in-depth with my project about hot fuel jet pipe electrohydraulic servo valves (EHSV) flow stability issues. I talked about my NASA Langley Research Center work and progressed into my grad school projects. I discussed my Electronic Warfare project, my Space Systems Mars Architecture work, and ended with my research about the Europa Clipper mission which was working with NASA JPL. At the end I had a final slide that recapped everything I had discussed, putting the key things I wanted them to take away and remember from the presentation.

Once I created the first draft of my presentation, I scheduled a time to practice my presentation to a room full of my graduate school friends. I asked them to "play as JPLers" to ask questions throughout and to also give me feedback on ways to improve. Constructive criticism was a tool I utilized often in finding ways to make myself better. I gave the presentation and received a lot of feedback. I mean a lot. Enough to make me feel slightly ill-prepared. "This is good though!" I thought to myself. What if I actually had that experience during the real event? I was glad to have had it prior to the big game. I knew I was going to need some help in this which is why I set up this mock presentation in the first place. I went in almost expecting to be torn apart by graduate school compatriots. There is always something to improve, and a room full of Georgia Tech Aerospace Engineering graduate students definitely did not disappoint in pointing those areas out. I went back to work revamping my presentation.

After I revised my massacred first draft per their feedback, I scheduled another mock presentation. I was extremely grateful that my reviewers took the time out of their busy days to help me out. Each of them had their own classes, research, and job searches. As payment, I bought each one of them lunch at their choice of food venue that was located on Georgia Tech's campus. I would say quite a small price to pay for the expertise I was receiving.

I was able to secure one of the large conference rooms for this one. The ASDL had two gigantic rooms for reviews and formal presentations. The projector screens inside are comparable to a movie theater. They were marvelous. One gigantic screen in the front and then two large projector screens on each side as well: two on the left wall and two on the right. On the remaining wall space lived fascinating aerospace designs. Some full plane pictures, others draft documents or computer simulation views. We went inside, turned down the lights, and I projected my slides up on the wall to one of the non-gigantic screens. As I presented, questions were asked and I fielded them well. This one went much smoother and only had minor corrections. I felt content with their feedback and confident that I had a strong presentation that showcased my wide range of skills and experience. Now the presentation was set. It was time to prep for the interview itself.

I started with researching typical interview questions and then searched online to see if I could find anyone talking about JPL specific interview questions. With the age of the internet, I was actually able to find typical JPL interview questions quite easily. I think it was GlassDoor.com where I found those listed by former JPL interviewees. The questions I found were: *Why should we hire you? What's your greatest weakness? If you came to JPL with an unlimited budget, what would you do? What is your favorite body in the Solar System? Where do you see yourself in five years? Ten years?* I took these questions, wrote them down, and then wrote out answers for each. The answers I planned for the first two questions are below:

1. Why should we hire you?

   a. That's a great question. I think that's why we're here, in fact—to determine whether I'm the right person for this job and whether you're the right organization for me. I honestly can't say that you should hire me because I don't know the culture and the goals here the way you do. You know the organization, you know yourself and your leadership style, and now you know a little about my background and my perspective. I'm confident you're going to hire the person who's the best fit for this position, and that if the universe wants the two of us to work together, it'll happen.

2. What's your greatest weakness?

   a. I may not always be able to write down the equation needed off the top of my head or recall from memory a specific value from something, but I've learned to always keep detailed and organized notes so that I always have something to reference to make sure that I am correct. I've summarized and organized my notes from my undergraduate work at Platteville and have held on to some important texts that prepared me for the FE exam.

I chose the first question's answer about hiring me because I felt that it was actually an honest, eye opening answer that they may not hear too often. Most people will tote their skills and how they know they will fit in and be a good employee. Where here, I acknowledged the power and experience of my interviewers. To the second question about weaknesses, you have to state weaknesses carefully. It is 100% OKAY to say your weaknesses, but it is also 100% CRUCIAL to end the answer with how you overcome, or how you are working to overcome, your stated weakness. My weakness actually shows a strength for organization, attention to detail, and double checking without assuming something to be true.

The unlimited budget question was somewhat of a fun one to answer. I would say that I wanted to send a triple-threat mission to Titan, one of the moons of Saturn that has liquid methane-ethane lakes. The triple threat would be a boat to land on the lakes, a rover to traverse the land, and a helicopter or airborne vehicle to travel the skies. Titan is a very interesting and diverse body that has not been explored in-situ that heavily. In-situ meaning having a spacecraft present on the surface instead of using remote sensing instruments form the distance of orbit. The probe named Huygens that rode along with the Cassini spacecraft that launched in 1997 was released and landed on the surface. Huygens provided amazing images and scientific data that showed Titan resembles what the Earth may have been like when life first formed. A primordial soup if you will. Cassini ended it's 20 year mission on September 15th, 2017 with a Grand Finale of ring grazing orbits diving between the rings and the planet Saturn itself. It performed 22 of these daring dives until its last one brought it into the atmosphere to end its mission.

For my favorite body in the Solar System, I said it was a tie between Titan and Europa. Europa was my JPL research project. It was my first real work with JPL so I considered it my baby. It is so interesting, one of the places with the highest potential to find life in our solar system outside of Earth. Europa is essentially a big ball of liquid water with a frozen icy crust as its surface. But underneath that ice surface is a vast ocean thought to have more than three times the water of Earth and it's only about the size of our moon.

The next thing to do was to establish a list of questions that I could ask during the course of the interviews. Of course I would not only pull from this list as I would choose questions based upon the conversations we were having and the things the interviewers said. However, I needed to be prepared with a list of questions that would be inquisitive and intriguing to the interviewers. I came up with 18 questions that I thought would do pretty well and show my curiosity.

1. What is the process and opportunities for advancement? Levels and timeframe? Where would I start?

2. What is the ease/capability to transfer departments within JPL?

3. Do you reward your employees for stuff like successful missions, papers, & such? Awards/$$?

4. What is the boss/employee relationship like? Open door, weekly tag-ups, etc.?

5. With the evolution of the workforce moving towards a younger generation, what do you have planned?

6. Are there any new trends in Systems Engineering that you see as promising and applicable to JPL?

7. I've read about a penetrator spacecraft, the Ice Pick Mission to Europa. How would this get around Europa's planetary protection? How does that work?

8. What skills and experiences would make an ideal candidate?

9. What is the single largest problem facing your staff and would I be in a position to help you solve this problem?

10. What constitutes success at this position and JPL in general? Project lifespans and quite long, what type of milestones do you track?

11. How did you become an employee of JPL?

12. What is your inspiration for aerospace? Do you have a defining moment?

13. What have you enjoyed most about working here? What is one thing you don't like or would improve?

14. What's your greatest professional accomplishment so far, and why?

15. Do you have any hesitations about my qualifications?

16. Do you offer professional training?

17. Can you tell me about the team I'll be working with? How many, age range?

18. Do you feel that I would fit well with you team? What is the next step in the process?

I wrote these down by hand into my portfolio that I would be carrying around with me. In my portfolio I would also have copies of my resume, references, transcripts, and other reference material. I made sure I had all my paperwork in line and ready just in case I needed to access any of it. My way to overcome my weakness I mentioned early—preparation. I even printed out my Matlab code for my genetic algorithm based on the second round interview where I was asked to discuss it in detail. I felt prepped with my presentation and my interview questions. I was ready to charge at JPL and get my dream job!

A Non-JPL Interview Surprise

During this prep time I was notified by the teaching assistants of Dr. Mavris that we could opt out of the finals and take our current grade. Who doesn't want to opt out of taking finals, so I grabbed all my assignments and a calculator. I calculated that I would have a B if I did that. A B-grade is above average and I was perfectly content with that grade. I emailed Dr. Mavris and told him that I would like to opt out of finals and take my B so that I could fully concentrate on preparing for my JPL interview. I reminded him that JPL was the ultimate dream job for me. He emailed back and was not in favor of this idea as he wanted me to take the finals and raise my grade up to an A. He saw potential for me to increase my grade and wanted me to take advantage of that. He said that it is still important to get the best grades possible, regardless of where you were in a job process. I think he may have known about what happened to me next, why he really wanted me to learn more of and secure my knowledge in aircraft design. That was the class he taught. However, we all know by this point that I am a space kid at heart.

One day, to my surprise, I received an email from Northrop Grumman in Los Angeles asking me for an interview. Northrop Grumman is a global aerospace and defense technology company and was named as the fifth-largest defense contractor in the world in 2015. I did apply online to the Space Systems department of Northrop Grumman, Boeing, and Lockheed Martin. Once I set my sights on JPL, I did not really follow-up on any of them. The email said that the job was about aircraft design. I didn't really want to work with aircraft design. Again I'm a space kid, but I did not want to just throw away another opportunity if JPL was not my career path. I still had Woodward in my back pocket, but Northrop was also in Los Angeles. That made southern California quite appealing to me. I set up a phone interview the next week. The day of the interview I found an empty conference room in the back of the ASDL and had the interview. I had my laptop in front of me with my resume and Northrop's website up. I also had my notepad to take notes with and a list of questions to ask.

I did not think the interview went that well because my heart was not truly in it. The passion was not there when responding to questions. To my surprise two weeks later I received a call from them to set up an on-site interview in Los Angeles. I was already booked up until the New Year with finals, the JPL interview, and Christmas break with my family. So we scheduled the interview right after Christmas break. Where once again I received a free flight from my home in Wisconsin to Los Angeles and then have them fly me back to Atlanta to start school. With this added interview I actually would be missing the first two days of school, but I emailed my professors to tell him this. Each one of them said a job interview was the perfect excuse to be absent. What they did not know was that I could have made it back for the first day, but I had Northrop book me an extra night in the hotel so that I could explore Los Angeles the day after my interview. Why not explore Los Angeles while in town? I was really working the system and saved hundreds of dollars on travel! I did not have to pay for my flight to or from home for Christmas.

On-Site at NASA JPL

FINAL EXAMS WENT smoothly and I did improve my grades from B's to A's. I packed up my belongings for Christmas break with my family and also my nicely ironed suit in its carrying case for my on-site JPL interview. I did not have a car for use in Atlanta so I was either walking, biking, or using public transit to get around.

Actually I stopped biking the semester of my JPL interviews, but not by choice. My bike was stolen out of the stairwell of my building, which is behind keycard access doors. I filed a police report and alerted the other members of the lab. It turns out that the keycard access door to that stairwell will just open if you pull on the door hard enough. Most likely someone got in that way. The strange thing was that in place of my bike, there was a brand new smaller bike with the tags still on it, a padlock around its chain, and a damaged pedal axle. I can only image that someone stole that bike from the store and for some reason decided to try and come in our locked stairwell exchanging it for my bike. Anyways, I took the train, hopped on the plane, and arrived in California ready for my next challenge.

As I was waiting in the JPL lobby, I looked at my interview schedule. I had four 1-hour interviews, my 1-hour presentation, a 1-hr tour, and a 1-hr lunch. Two of my four 1-hr interviews would be with two people and the other two were with just one interviewer. I only had one interview with Department 31, the second department that called me, and the other three were with Department 39. I started off with the Department 31 interview, Project Formulation. This is the department I actually preferred to be hired into if I had a choice. I was slightly disappointed to see only one interview with them. I was hoping for more. I needed to rock this first interview so well that he would see enough potential in me to relay it to the rest of his department.

I was escorted to the 31 interview. I walked into a four-walled office next to a group of cubicles. A shorter balding man about 45 years old sat behind a desk. He stood up and smiled, introduced himself and asked me to take a seat. We started off with small talk for the first five minutes before going into the typical interview format. He described to me what his group specifically did, some of the projects they were working on, and then dove into my resume to inquire about its contents. I felt like the interview went very well. He then walked me across the street to my next interview in a different building. I needed to be escorted at all times on JPL's campus for security reasons and I also had no idea where I was going. NASA JPL was a huge area, to the point where it felt like a college campus. There were about 5,000 employees and over 50 buildings. During the walk I decided to take this opportunity to ask for feedback. I asked my interviewer how he thought the interview went and if there were any points where I could have improved. He said the interview went very well and that nothing stood out to him as a weakness. I asked what the next steps were and he stated that he would have to talk to others in the department and figure out their funding situation if they were able to hire more members. At this point we were now at the office of my second interview. We shook hands, I said "Thank You", and he went back to his building.

I continued with the second interview for another hour which also seemed to go pretty well. This one was with a member of the spacecraft Juno team. Juno is one of NASA JPL's spacecrafts that was on its way to Jupiter at the time. It went into orbit around Jupiter on July 4th, 2016. A little nerd humor here. Jupiter was named after the king of the Roman gods. Juno was the name of his wife. The four largest moons of Jupiter are named Io, Europa, Ganymede, and Callisto which received their names as the extramarital lovers of Jupiter. NASA JPL sent Juno to watch over Jupiter and keep an eye on his mistresses. NASA does one of two things when naming missions: 1) they either have an acronym or 2) they play to a hidden or extended meaning of sorts. The interview was again fun, emphasizing the relationship employees have loving their job. This made me feel relaxed which I needed because next was the presentation. This was what I was most nervous about.

I was guided to the room which was back in the first building I had my interview in. It was a conference room with a long table in the center that sat about ten people, five on each side, but no one was there yet besides me. At the far end of the room was a projection screen hanging down from the ceiling. The projector itself hung like a stalagmite from the center of the ceiling against the wall. I reached into my backpack, pulled out my computer, and started to set up hoping for no technical difficulties. I had two versions of my presentation. One was in a Microsoft PowerPoint format that had animations in it and the other was a strict PDF with no animations in case the system was not compatible with my PC PowerPoint format. I tested the animation format and it worked perfectly. Technical glitches are all too common in times of importance so I was quite happy and relieved to see my first version worked just fine.

Soon a few people came into the room. The first man I interviewed with, two other gentlemen, and my second interviewer from the Juno team. It was ten minutes past the hour and they suggested I get started. I was expecting there to be more people present for my presentation, but I did not complain. I saw it as less reviewers meant I could have a stronger and more engaging relationship with a small set of people than a wide audience. Everything in the presentation went smoothly, no hiccups. In the beginning where I stated a little bit about myself and that I was into fitness and eating healthy, one of the other gentlemen that joined slid a candy bar down the table to me. We all shared a laugh and that engaged a great start.

Once I actually started presenting I was not nervous anymore. I was focused, in the game and ready to showcase myself. I discussed my internships and was asked a few questions as I went through. I answered them confidently and moved on with the presentation. One of the questions was regarding my hot fuel jet pipe electrohydraulic servo valves (EHSV) flow stability issue project. One of the other gentlemen asked me to elaborate on the flow instability issue and what other approaches were considered before experimenting with the one I chose. I discussed how I brainstormed solutions to the problem without considering constraints to not limit my imagination. Then I added in constraints, eliminating parts of the trade space, and downselected to the solution I moved forward with in my experiment.

I finished just shy of my one hour allotted time, leaving room for a couple post-presenting questions. A perfectly timed presentation in my book that went according to plan. Now it was on to lunch. They set me up to go to lunch with someone who had been recently hired and went through the same interview process. My lunch buddy was an MIT graduate who was very nice and friendly. We had a good conversation and I picked his brain about his interview process. He told me that he actually received two offers from two different departments. He was so good that both departments wanted him. Inside I was secretly thinking, hoping that I would be in his same situation in a couple weeks since I also had two departments fly me out to interview. My hopes were high.

After lunch was the NASA JPL campus tour. We had an hour and were taken to two places. First was to Von Karman Museum, which has models of each spacecraft JPL has built. All of them are in order of the Solar System. It starts with the Sun and as your progress around the room you move from planet to planet: Mercury, Venus, Earth, Mars, the asteroid belt, Jupiter, Saturn, Uranus, Neptune, to the Kuiper Belt with Pluto, and then outside of the Solar System. They also had grey spheres to represent the planets to scale to each other starting with the sun which was painted on the wall. The sun was larger than my wingspan at 6'4" and Earth was smaller than a golf ball. It was an amazing room full of so many engineering marvels. It was a beautiful sight.

In the room next door they had a full size model of Voyager, a pair of twin spacecrafts that have ventured further away from Earth than anything ever human made. It had a large ~3m antenna dish in the center with two booms projecting off of it. One boom is for an instrument called a magnetometer which needs to be away from the spacecraft to take its measurements accurately. The other boom is for the power source: three RTG's or Radioisotope Thermoelectric Generators. These RTG's are powered by decaying Plutonium-238. As the Plutonium-238 decays it releases heat, and this heat is converted into electricity to power the spacecraft. Along with Voyager was sent a golden record, "Sounds of Earth." Where an actual record containing sounds of Earth, "hello" in several languages, and music (Johnny B. Goode by Chuck Barry is on it) was sent with a record player. On the outside of the box are instructions for the record as well as a map of where it came from with well-studied pulsar stars. If intelligent life was to find Voyager and see the golden record, they would be able to determine where it came from and also how to play the record. NASA sent us out into the universe!

The next and last stop on the tour was the Spacecraft Flight Operations Facility or SFOF because NASA loves its acronyms.

This building is mission control for all of the robotic spacecraft exploring out at the moon and beyond. It's a darkly lit room that gets most of its light from the computer monitors and screens projecting information. Screens showing which spacecraft is communicating with Earth at the given time and computer visuals showing where it is in space. There are desks and tables as you would imagine thinking of a mission control room. Each desk is assigned to a certain spacecraft and there a person called an ACE sends commands to the spacecraft to control it. In the center of the room is a small glass floor and underneath this little glass window is a plaque that reads "The Center of the Universe." All the information coming from spacecrafts out exploring from the moon and beyond comes through this room, so essentially it could be thought of as the center of the universe in terms of collecting information by humans. One of the directors of JPL named Charles Elachi said this room was the center of the universe to some special guests once. The head of the SFOF Jim McClure thought to himself "Oh my, the director just lied to his guests!" He then took it upon himself to actually create this "Center of the Universe" monument so that Dr. Charles Elachi would be telling the truth.

In a room next to the spacecraft mission control is another mission control room that is used for critical events, such as landing on Mars. Here each seat has a name assigned to it. One for the Administrator of NASA, one for the Director of JPL, and many more important members of the NASA family as well as the essential personnel for the spacecraft operations. For our tour, we got to sit in these seats and put on the headsets that these members would wear during the critical events. We watched a computer simulated video of the Mars rover

Curiosity landing and took some pictures celebrating as if it were happening in real time. It was a nice break from the long, intensive interviews we were partaking in. A good smile and laugh goes a long way.

On to the last two hours of the interview day. Each of these two interviews were supposed to be with two interviewers. However, one of the interviewers was out sick so my next interview was with just one man, one of the gentlemen who attended my presentation. His name was Tom and we shared a similar height. He was bald, no glasses, but had a look of wisdom to himself. He was the section manager for one of the sections in department 39. His interview tactic started out by going for a walk to one of the two Starbucks coffee carts on JPL's campus. He bought me a coffee and then we sat outside for the first 20 minutes at a table. This was a nice gesture and a good break from the typical interview format. He said that he understands what us interviewees go through and a coffee is well deserved towards the end of the day. After the 20 minutes was up, he took me on another little tour. We went to the high bays, which is where the spacecraft actually gets assembled. These are clean rooms that monitor the amount of dust, humidity, and temperature of a large room. JPL needs to maintain certain conditions for their spacecraft parts as they build and prepare them for launch. My interviewer told me about these buildings and what he worked on that has been in them. I asked questions about his projects to get him to further elaborate; again, showing my inquisitive side and that I wanted to learn.

On our walk back to his building to bring me to my next interview, he asked the typical where do you see yourself in five, ten year questions. I responded with the answers that I prepped out, but he inquired more, trying to gain a real sense of what I want to do. I dug deep for a response and came up with something to the order of "Well, I guess the exact spot I see myself in will change as I learn about JPL in my first few years. I am not familiar with all the possibilities available to me since I have not experienced the JPL day-to-day operations. I would strive to learn as much as I can when I start so that I determine what type of career path is most appropriate for me within JPL in the coming years." He liked that response and said that as people progress through their careers, they learn what they like and what they don't like which shapes their career decisions along the way.

I then asked my last question, "How do you think this interview went? Was there anything you thought I could improve upon?" First off, he complimented me for asking for feedback. Next, he said everything went pretty well, but he would suggest one thing that was actually during my presentation. He suggested that I dove down deeper into the details of some of my design problems, go with a more technical approach to show the nitty, gritty, down in the weeds work I had to do in order to solve my problems. He said that would have played to my strength of technical ability and showcase my "time in the trenches" that I know down to the equation what causes problems and how I addressed them. This feedback point made a lot of sense to me at that moment, as in the beginning of our interview with coffee he asked me to elaborate on one of the mechanical issues with a fuel valve I solved during one of my Woodward internships. So there was my first improvement needed/weakness of the day that I was told, but he followed it up with a couple compliments and said it was a pleasure meeting and talking with me. I felt confident again as we parted ways.

Alright now it was time to finish the day strong with a dual interviewer interview. This one was with a man and a woman who worked under the section manager I was just with. The man here is the one who slid the candy bar during my presentation. The whole interview had a great, high energy, enjoyable mood. They asked a few questions, but really wanted to give me the chance to ask as many questions of them as I could. One question I recall the candy bar man asked was "What is one of your weaknesses?" I decided to respond with "My computer coding is not that advanced. I know a few languages, but I need to increase my abilities in them." He responded with "Ah that's no problem, I need to do that too, haha. We all learn to increase our abilities as we go along. What else?" Here is where I responded with my prepared answer I told you about earlier—not being able to rattle off an equation, but keeping detailed notes to reference. They really liked that answer and said it was actually a good trait of a systems engineer to have those types of information available and organized. Perfect! I was successful at demonstrating my weakness as a strength.

I asked them their stories of how they got into JPL and both of them actually had jobs elsewhere first and then came to JPL mid-career. They said that might have to be a route for some people since JPL is a highly desired place to work and only the best of the best get in on the first try. They gave me some insight into different ways to get into JPL besides this first interview processes. A thought that had not really occurred to me: work elsewhere for a couple years and then try to transfer in. Almost like my thoughts with Georgia Tech when I was initially rejected.

The last interview was over and I was escorted to the security gate where I dropped off my visitor badge. We shook hands, he said he'd be in touch, we smiled, and went our separate ways. I walked out confident and hopeful with a tremendous smile and feel of relief as my third round of an all-day interview was complete. Now was the "waiting game" as people say. However I am not one to just play the "waiting game." I realized I had made a mistake and not asked for business cards of the interviewers throughout the course of the day. I wanted to write a thank you email for the interviews, but lacked their contact information. What I did have was their names and their department numbers at JPL. I set out on a Google escapade to find their email addresses. Scientists and engineers publish papers, especially at NASA, and present those papers at conferences so there must be a trace online of these interviewers with their NASA affiliation. I was able to find all but one of them. With Christmas approaching I wanted them to keep me in their mind right away and hopefully get back to me with an offer before Christmas. I sat in the airport the next day, wrote my thank you emails and sent them over the airport Wi-Fi which took forever to do. I boarded my plane having set more things in motion, engaging my interviewers once again showing initiative and persistence. My hopes were still high and I was excited to hear back.

12

JPL Failure,
GA Tech Success

EACH AND EVERY single day after that I was anxious to receive a call or an email back. I was constantly checking to see if something had been received, but no luck. I was now back in Wisconsin with my family and during this time I was working out at my home gym, the Heart of the Valley YMCA in Kimberly, WI. I became good friends with one of the front desk workers, Dan, an older man in his 60's who's been already calling me a rocket scientist for a while once he learned I was in grad school for aerospace engineering. I informed him of my JPL interview and that I was waiting to hear back. So each day when I went to the gym and saw him at the front desk, he would get happy, smile, and ask "So did you hear yet?!" Seeing other people excited for me was an excellent feeling. My potential success was creating excitement and happiness in others. But each day I had to say, "Nope, not yet. But I have a good feeling that today might be the day!" I always kept my head and hopes high, holding a positive attitude for the outcome.

I went through Christmas and New Years without hearing anything. I would be having my Northrop Grumman interview soon and have not heard from JPL. I thought to myself, this could be a good thing. If I nail the Northrop interview and get an offer, when JPL calls I would have some negotiating power to get a better salary if I had another job offer on the table. So it was back to Los Angeles for another interview.

I flew out of Appleton, WI and into Los Angeles Airport (LAX), got my rental car, and headed to the hotel. This hotel was a lot more than I expected. I expected the same as JPL where it was a one room hotel room. But to my surprise it was essentially a studio apartment. I had a living room, a dining table, a kitchen, the works! It was a pretty sweet setup. I unpacked as I was going to be there for two nights and three days.

As I drove up to Northrop Grumman the next day I had no idea where to go. The site was huge and had multiple gates and entrances. I finally tried to go in one and asked a guard where I should be going for an interview. He pointed me in the right direction and which gate I was supposed to go into. So I pulled a U-turn and headed towards where I was supposed to be. I drove in the gate, got approved by the guard, and parked my car. Northrop is set south of LA in El Segundo which has more of an industrial feel to it. The Northrop campus had very large warehouse style buildings and seemed like more of a manufacturing plant, which is what it was. I checked into the visitor's building which was more of a trailer near the front gate. About ten minutes later my escort came and picked me up as she was also to be my first interviewer. This interview was only scheduled to be four hours long, half of that of the JPL interview. I had just experienced the JPL process and felt that only four hours would be a breeze in comparison.

Northrop definitely had more of a private industry feel. It's hard to describe in words, but the feeling of walking around NASA versus walking around private companies is just different. NASA feels more open, relaxed, and friendly. Where the private companies seem stricter, quiet, and consumer driven. The offices seemed stuffy and small. The area just did not feel "right" for me, but I went on with the interview in confidence to get the job and use it as leverage against JPL. As I mentioned earlier, this interview was for aircraft design projects and it did not really hit home with me, but I used my training and education from the ASDL to communicate effectively. The conversations went well but where I believe a disconnect happened is that the ASDL teaches new advanced design methods and it did not seem that Northrop was on board to use these new methods in the projects they were looking to hire for. I explained my training and its utility and could not seem to convince them of its effectiveness. The ASDL technique is a paradigm shift and most industry leaders that I've experienced, almost fear change and it seemed like I was in that environment. Almost a "if it's not broke, don't fix it" type of environment instead of a "if it could be better, it might as well be broken" environment.

At the end of the interview, though, it did seem like all things went well. They did appreciate a new viewpoint on the design process, but said it may be difficult to get others on board with it. They did say that I had the skills necessary to do the job they were looking for and that I would be good at it. This gave me a little faith in receiving an offer, but not a strong confidence in one given the disconnect of the new design methods. I did follow up, but with my heart not being in it. I was definitely not as persistent as I was with JPL or Georgia Tech. I ultimately did not end up hearing back from Northrop, not even to tell me that I was not selected for the job. Just radio silence.

JPL was my only hope and I was still waiting to hear back, but again I did not just wait. I continued to follow-up with emails asking for a status update and even made a couple phone calls to one of the interviewers and left voicemails. Then I finally received a phone call back. I was at a Georgia Tech basketball game with some of my ASDL friends when my phone started to vibrate. The game had not started yet and it was not extremely loud in the arena so I answered it. Once I found out who it was I immediately ran up the stairs and out to the concession stand area to find a quieter place to talk. I found a smaller quiet hallway and continued the conversation.

My heart was racing fast. I'm nervous, excited, and scared all at the same time. This is when I heard something that made my heart sink, "We thought you were great, but we feel that you lack the experience required for the job we are looking to hire for, I'm sorry." I said "Okay thank you for getting back to me and letting me know. Can I ask one more question?" He responded with "Sure" and I asked "Was there anything else that I could improve upon besides the lack of specific experience for the job?" He replied with "Umm, nothing really sticks out. We think you had a great interview, it's just the specific skills for operations we did not see." I ended the short conversation with "Okay, thank you sir and have a good night."

I returned to my friends by the basketball court and they asked who it was. I told them, one of them being an already future JPL employee, that it was JPL and they said I did not get the job. They felt my disappointment, but the one who already had a JPL job and connections there said "Don't worry, we'll figure something out to get you in. We can probably get you an internship and then you can prove yourself with actual work there." He had mentioned this to me when I was preparing my presentation since it is extremely hard to get into JPL without having an internship with them first. He said that it would not be the end of the road if I did not make it on the first try. I did not see that as an option in my mind though. If I would have thought like that, I would have most likely not poured as much effort into the process as I did. I went through the first try as it would be the one and only try. Now that the first try had failed, it was on to the next route to figure out what I would have to do. It wasn't just that easy for me to receive an internship though.

In order to receive an internship at JPL you have to be a continuing student, meaning that you will return to school after the internship ends. I was on track to graduate with my ASDL classmates in spring 2015, just a couple months away, and wanted to walk the stage and celebrate with all of them. I was asked by a JPL contact, who had an internship opportunity available, if I would be willing to defer graduation until December so that I could take the internship. I said yes, but I really did not want to and sought to find another way. So I decided to see what else I could figure out to allow me to graduate with my friends, but still be qualified for an internship. Then an idea popped in my head. I was in a graduate program that had Masters and PhD students. I was just finishing my Master's degree, but so were many others that were actually continuing on to work on their PhD. They were walking the stage at graduation to complete the first part of their grad school, then continue on with their PhD work. I thought this was the perfect opportunity to take advantage of to get myself qualified as a returning student.

I thought about the PhD before entering graduate school. I ultimately decided that I would be able to do what I wanted to do with a Master's degree. I did not have one special topic that really resonated with me to focus on a PhD thesis. Therefore I never planned to actually go into the PhD program with my advisor, Dr. Mavris a.k.a. Doc. I emailed Doc, told him about my situation and the idea I had. He agreed to it and that meant that on paper it would state that I would return to the ASDL in the fall after having graduated with my Masters to start the PhD program. We both knew that this was not an option for me, but it would grant me the qualification I needed for the internship. My JPL contact was on board with this as well, but we could not let the JPL Education Office in on our little plan because it would disqualify me for the internship. If I received a job offer I could say something to the order of "Now having industry experience, I prefer to continue my career in industry instead of pursuing my PhD."

So there we go, I did the riskiest thing I've ever done in my life. I decided to graduate without a job and take a 10-week temporary internship in hopes that I would be able to prove myself to JPL and get hired as a fulltime employee before my time was up. If I was not successful, I was headed back to

Kaukauna, WI to live with my parents and figure things out at that time. I did have a fallback option or a Plan B if everything did fall apart. I would joke with people that I would become a beach bum and said it could be worse, but that was just that, a joke. My true plan B was to go back to Woodward, Inc. and ask for a job. They had offered me a job after my third internship while I was out at my NASA Langley Research Center internship. I had to decline that offer since the NASA co-op pushed my graduation back nine months. Then knowing that my graduation was delayed, they offered me an internship for the following summer and I took that just in case NASA was not able to bring me back. If NASA had a spot from me I would withdraw from the internship. However, Langley was not able to bring me back, so that's how I went back and did a fourth internship with Woodward. During that time is when I applied and eventually got accepted into Georgia Tech. My Woodward bosses and contacts told me that there would always be a job for me there if I wanted it. They even gave me another job offer during that summer despite me telling them that I was going on to graduate school. This was the card I had in my back pocket if everything fell apart, but I was driven to never have to pull out that card and succeed at Plan A. My heart and passion was going to push me and I would achieve my dream.

The start of the internship was to be June 1st, 2015. That was a few months away and I still had to get through my last semester of graduate school at Georgia Tech in the ASDL. I was still working on my JPL research project on Europa Clipper and was heavily involved with getting work done on that. EAB, the External Advisory Board, review that I was an observer at during my first semester was coming up as well. This time, however, I was going to be the one up in front presenting our research results to the room of important people with the purse strings to fund the lab. I spent countless hours preparing the presentation and practicing. This presentation was going to be about 30 minutes long, with then ten minutes for questions. I was going to give the first 15 minutes of the presentation as the Project Manager and the Chief Engineer of the team would take over and discuss the remaining. After the 30 minutes, we would both stand up and take questions. We practiced this presentation in full over ten times in the last few months leading up to EAB.

I was taking classes, but fortunately none of my classes in this last semester had in-class final exams. They were all final presentations or research projects instead of a paper exam. I preferred that method. I felt more comfortable with presenting and researching than to study for hours and then answer some questions on paper. I had three final presentations including EAB, a good amount of information and speaking to juggle, but I felt comfortable with it. During my time in the ASDL I became a master of PowerPoint presentations. Almost every other week I had to give a presentation and practice communicating effectively. Nine times out of ten it was presenting the EAB slides we had prepared and iterating on them until they were perfect. I learned that a visual aid goes a long way in relaying a concept to someone who is unfamiliar with it. Also how to tell a story in an efficient fashion of a technical research project to someone who is not an expert in the field of the research I was conducting.

The EAB room was going to be filled with a bunch of professionals from many different industries. The fundamental advanced knowledge and appreciation was there in each member, but they did not necessarily have any experience in what I would be talking about. The challenge was to convey the complex problem not too difficult and detailed, but also not to be too simple and easy. It needed to be right in the middle, a Goldilocks problem. If I spoke too detailed and used specific language only known to members of the research industry, it would go over the heads of the EAB members and I would not be able to connect with them. If I spoke too simple and easy, it could relay that the problem was too simple or it could come off as "here's a dumbed down version because you aren't smart enough to understand." So the Goldilocks problem was to connect with them and make them understand the problem while relaying the advanced complexity of the problem but not in too much detail.

EAB was on April 28th and 29th of 2015. The first day was to be our normal presentation that we were practicing to present to the whole board. The second day was a breakout session, where we would meet with our sponsors and go into depth of our research results. The Chief Engineer and I found an empty room in the basement of the ASDL in the morning and practiced our presentation. We were scheduled to present about 11:00 am. So there we were at 9:00am in the basement, in a room alone, dressed in our suits and ties giving a presentation to the wall. We went through it just fine and got the initial jitters out of the way. 11:00 am approached and we were ready.

I was seated in the back waiting my turn. The team before us ended and we approached the front. EAB was in the large conference rooms of the ASDL with the movie theater sized projection screens. Standing up in front, I looked out into the audience of approximately 50 individuals dressed in suits and ties or business casual attire. I stood with a smile, put on my lapel microphone and went to town. I remember standing up there looking into the audience making eye contact as I went through my slides. I was essentially reciting it from memory since I've done it so many times it was just a reflex at this point. I rarely turned my head towards the projector screen to look at the slides. As I went through, I clicked the little clicker in my hand to advance the slides and it went perfectly. My hands were not sweaty, my heart was not racing, I felt calm and relaxed because I knew my material. I was the expert in it.

After all of the presentations were over on the first day, all of the presenters get called back up to the front of the room and each EAB member gave the group about 30 seconds of feedback. 99.9% of the feedback is positive, everyone is greatly impressed with what we as a lab are able to accomplish and provide to our sponsors. When it came time for our JPL contact to speak, he said something I will never forget. He said that I conveyed the science of our project with a passion and knowledge that was equal to that of the actual NASA JPL project scientist. I was extremely taken back and went "Whoa" inside my head while a huge smile came across my face. An amazing compliment to boost my confidence in my knowledge of my research. This was the same JPL contact that had given me my internship. He told me later during the internship that he saw something special in me and needed to do what he could to get me into

JPL so they could experience me first hand just like he had. He did not have the ability to hire, otherwise I think I would not have had a problem getting that full time job the first time around.

Graduation was just a few days later on May 1st, 2015. I had two graduation ceremonies to attend. The first was the ASDL only graduation where our lab director and advisor Dr. Mavris put together a hooding ceremony for all of us ASDLers. It was in the presidential press box of the football stadium overlooking the field. It was a pretty enjoyable view. There were tables with appetizers and sandwiches on them as you entered the room. I went and took my seat with my fellow ASDLers and the ceremony began. My name was called and I walked up the front to be hooded. I am quite tall at 6 foot 4 inches, where my advisor is about 5 foot 6 or 8. So when I got to the front, I turned around in front of him to be hooded and dropped to my knees so that he could reach over my head to perform the hooding.

After the ASDL hooding ceremony was complete, I ventured down to the basketball stadium for the campus wide graduate school graduation ceremony. The same basketball court where I had received a phone call from JPL crushing my dreams for an instant by not giving me a fulltime job. But that thought was not in my head, it was in the past. I had plans to move forward and get that job, so to dwell in the past is useless. Looking back, I do find it significant that I am graduating from a school that initially rejected me at the location that NASA JPL initially rejected me. I sat down on the court with my fellow Georgia Tech graduate students. Looking to my left I can see my family:

mom, dad, brother, and sister. All traveled one thousand miles to share this moment with me. They took pictures of me sitting there—I made some funny faces. It was a joyous occasion. The ceremony started and we were under way. Eventually it was my turn to go across the stage and receive my diploma. I'm standing in line on the side, waiting to hear my name, a constant smile on my face. The joy inside of me was unreal, I had accomplished my goal of graduating from Georgia Tech. While I was waiting for my name to be called I thought back to the email I received just two years earlier denying me entrance to the school. I laughed at that. I was rejected from entering and then went on to get a full ride tuition and paid stipend. What a turn of events. It really shows that if you follow up, ask for feedback, and continue to inquire, be persistent and sincere, that you can achieve anything. I knew that I had to take this exact approach for the 10-week JPL internship. If I was able to do this with Georgia Tech, I could get myself a job at NASA JPL. And then I heard it, "Kevin J. DeBruin."

I stepped on that stage with a strong presence and an even stronger smile. The entire basketball arena was filled with students, friends and family members cheering as each name was read. The Georgia Tech graduation ceremony is even broadcasted live online where hundreds, if not thousands, of aspiring students tune in. A story was told of an international student that witnessed the ceremony many years ago through his computer and dreamed of one day walking that stage himself. Today was that day. An extraordinary story that really put into perspective how big of a deal graduating from Georgia Tech was to the whole world.

My NASA JPL internship was to start on June 1st, 2015. After graduation, I drove back from Atlanta with my mom, dad, and sister in the blue Equinox to our home in Kaukauna, Wisconsin. My brother flew back because he had to get back to work. I was able to spend a few weeks with them before I had to move out to Los Angeles and start another journey. It was an amazing time to be able to relax and take a breath after finishing graduate school. It had been a 16 month sprint. I remember counting it up once, my numbers may not be exact anymore, but I figured out that out of 16 months I was there, there were only about 30 days I was not in the lab working or working remotely from Wisconsin. That 30 days included holidays, weekends, and traveling for trips back home too.

There was still one important thing to do before I moved to California, I needed to find a place to live. I had a place lined up, but the guy ceased contact with me and I could not get ahold of him. I could not wait any longer and needed to take action and find a new place. I had some difficulty and up until the day before I was to fly out I planned on staying in a hotel for a few days to find a place. I tried Craigslist listings and came up empty, but I also put my own wanted-ad on Craigslist hoping to possibly hear something. I was with my family driving down to Milwaukee from Kaukauna to go to a Brewers game and then fly out in the morning when my phone rang. It ended up being a lady from Craigslist who was in need of someone to help out around the house since she broke her foot and she came across my posting. We ended up coming to an agreement pretty quickly. Another challenge tackled, the day before I moved to California I found a place to live.

When I moved out there I rented a car from RelayRides.com which was actually decently affordable. I was fed up with public transportation, biking, and walking from my time in Atlanta and my first month in Virginia. I wanted to have the freedom and independence in my transportation. I drove to work, parked in the West parking lot and headed towards the Visitor Center to check in for orientation. I did this same process just six months earlier with the thought of having a fulltime job eight hours later, but this time I would have ten weeks to make that happen.

NASA or Bust in 10-Weeks

JUNE 1ST, 2015: The first day in my 10-week timeframe to prove to JPL they could not live without me. On the first day, I had orientation for about two hours in the morning going through your typical company policies, resources, and such. We sat in the cool museum building I toured before with the large spacecraft models. Afterwards I was picked up by my mentor who was my JPL contact from before at Georgia Tech. He brought me to my office which was in the same building I had the majority of my interviews back in December. My office was a cubicle that I shared with two other interns. Three chairs in each of the three corners with the 4th corner being the doorway into the cube. They really crammed us in there together. You couldn't push your chair back too far, otherwise you would bump into your cubemates. This cubicle was actually just 20 feet away from one of my interviewers too, the one who bought me coffee. My mentor gave me a few resources to review for my summer project. I actually knew what my project was a couple months before starting. This next part might be a little dense, heck a lot dense for most people, as I describe a little bit about what my internship actually was in terms of my project. Apologies in advance for the jargon. Get ready for some rocket science.

For the JPL internship program I was a part of, you are required to submit a plan for your work with a schedule before arriving at JPL. I was going to be using a computer language that was being developed at JPL to model requirements for the Europa Clipper Mission. My graduate school research project was about the Europa Clipper, so I was quite familiar with the mission and the spacecraft. This language that was being developed at JPL was in its infancy and I was to help it grow and develop by putting it to use to demonstrate its utility while also addressing any issues along the way. This language was known as the K-Language. It is essentially a formal text language, like Python/Matlab/Fortran, in which you are able to model SysML (Systems Modeling Language) as opposed to using a visual modeling tool. As an extremely quick description, SysML is a general-purpose modeling language for Systems Engineering applications. It supports the specification, analysis, design, verification and validation of a broad range of systems and systems-of-systems. Basically it's a set of guidelines and processes on how to model a design. SysML is normally implemented via graphical programs such as MagicDraw or Rhapsody, but the K-Language allowed it to be implemented in a formal text approach instead.

Aerospace systems are complex systems that have interacting disciplines and technologies. With this multidisciplinary environment, there are numerous requirements that need to be checked against during the design process. This process is known as validation to answer the question "did you build the right thing?". This question is driven by the customer. It is desired to bring in the validation of requirements as early as possible. Early and ongoing validation of requirements leads to reduced errors in the complex system. There are hundreds of requirements when designing a spacecraft and there was no way I was to do all of them. I sat with my mentor and selected two top level concepts to investigate and model them and their child requirements. I modeled the "Gravity Science Concept" & "Deep Space Network (DSN) Missed Pass on Approach" requirements.

What is Gravity Science you may wonder. The tidal forces from Jupiter are thought to cause Europa to flex, deforming the shape of the body. The presence of a liquid ocean or differing thicknesses in the ice shell of Europa's crust determine how much the tidal deformations would be. If there is a liquid ocean the deformations would be larger than if Europa was solid ice or rock; this depends on the shear modulus of the material. This tidal deformation causes the gravity field around Europa to change. The investigation of gravity science aims to measure these differences in Europa's orbit around Jupiter by sensing small variations in acceleration during the flyby. The spacecraft itself cannot detect these small changes, however, very small accelerations can be detected by using radio signal measurements. Doppler tracking between the flight system and Earth is used to determine the delta of the spacecraft's predicted perfect path to its actual path due with deflection. The result of this measurement is a change in velocity or delta-V.

Now what does "Deep Space Network (DSN) Missed Pass on Approach" mean? The Deep Space Network, known as the DSN, is a network of antenna in three locations around the world which are used to communicate with all spacecrafts from out at the moon to beyond and out of our solar system. The three stations are at Goldstone, California; Madrid, Spain; and Canberra, Australia. This way at any time, a spacecraft can see at least one of the three antenna stations. At each station there is one 70-meter diameter antenna and at least four 34-meter diameter antennas. When a spacecraft is in lock and communication with an antenna it is known as a Pass; think of it as the spacecraft is Pass'ing overhead. While is it "pass'ing" overhead, it is sending the data it collected down to earth and is being caught by one of the large antennas. If for some reason the Europa Clipper was unable to create lock or missed a communication window with the DSN, it would need to have a plan. That is what the requirement "Deep Space Network (DSN) Missed Pass on Approach" was all about, the ability to plan for a missed communication period with the spacecraft.

I had to write a final report of my internship project. It was titled *Modeling Requirements Checking with the K Language for the Europa Project* and its abstract was:

Research into the possibility of modeling requirements checking with the K language was conducted. The K language is in development at JPL where it is essentially a version of SysML with a text format; a modeling language backed by formal model checkers like Google Z3 from Microsoft. There are two strong desires to result from this work. The first being that it will provide more concrete consequences of different ways of expressing requirements. The impacts to what instances are able to be created will be shown immediately, if any instances can be created from the set of requirements. The second being that of improving the definition of the requirements assisting in developing good requirements. Definition of a good requirement being a requirement having enough precision so that it can be calculated/modeled. If a requirement is able to be simulated, it can be tested. Two concepts for the Europa Project were modeled: 1) Gravity Science and 2) Missing a Single Planned DSN Pass.

So day in and day out for the first five weeks that was all I did. I arrived at my crowded grey walled cube, I put my head down and grinded like crazy to produce results early and show my work ethic. I didn't slack or joke around with my cubemates too much as I was on a mission. They were still in school and each had a few years left before graduation. As part of my grind I needed to work with the experts and gather the right information to incorporate into my project. I went and met with several people working on the Clipper project during this time. I gathered information, met new people and networked. This also showed initiative of going out and investigating the problem instead of waiting around for direction from my mentor. I knew that I was going to have to establish a reputation for myself before going around and asking for a fulltime job, so that's what I did. I built a reputation of taking initiative, eagerness and excitement, a go-getter, a hard worker, and the ability to complete tasks efficiently with little direction. Once that fifth week mark hit, I started to actively investigate the possibilities of a fulltime job.

I needed to know who had the actual ability to hire. I needed to speak with the right people. I found an organizational chart, talked to a few full timers, and figured out that Group Supervisors had that ability. The organization of JPLer's is in a matrix structure. There are departments; in departments are divisions; in divisions are sections; and in sections there are groups. Each group had a manager known as a Group Supervisor. These Group Supervisors act like talent agents renting you out to different projects that need personnel. A project will list positions needed and the Group Supervisors and Section Managers will fill those positions with their members.

I also learned that Group Supervisors like to have you interact with other members of their group and members of potential projects to see if you get along well and if you would be a good fit for the work and the environment. I set out to go and meet all the group supervisors of the Project Formulation division because that is where my true interest lied; Division 31 from which I only had one interview with earlier.

I used the JPL intranet to look up where the group supervisor's offices were. I would go there, knock on the door and introduce myself. I would say "Hi, my name is Kevin DeBruin and I am currently an intern here. I was wondering if I could set up a meeting with you to discuss the possibility of a full time job because I just graduated with my Masters in Aerospace Engineering." Every group supervisor I asked, responded with yes and asked me to please set up a meeting. I thanked them and then headed back to my desk to access Microsoft Outlook to setup the meeting. I titled the subject of every meeting to be "Hire Kevin Chat" so they knew exactly what my intentions where. With every meeting invite I also included a copy of my resume as well.

I met with about ten Group Supervisors and about 15 other members of their groups over the course of about three weeks to see how I would fit in and function in the dynamic. I also chose to go and introduce myself to the bosses of the Group Supervisors known as Section Managers. I knocked and walked into their offices, introduced myself, and told them that I was meeting with their Group Supervisors trying to get a full time job. I said I thought it would be nice to meet you and let you know what I was doing. This gave the Section Managers a face to put with the name when the Group Supervisors would bring me up in a monthly Group Supervisor and Section Manager meeting. This also showed the Section Managers my initiative to actively pursue a job and seek out the right people to make that happen.

There was one group that I wanted to be a part of over every other. That one was the Advanced Design Engineering group. It housed the members of the advanced design teams which used concurrent engineering. Concurrent engineering is engineering done in parallel instead of in series. The historic design process is that one person does work and then gives their results to another to use for their work via email, paper, or word of mouth. This process is continued on for the next person to do their work on a project. Concurrent engineering has all the members of the team in the same room at the same time to get everyone on the same page, have the right conversations together, answer questions as a team, and converge quickly on a design. These advanced design teams were the first group of people to tackle a problem, essentially starting from a blank piece of paper and a question. These teams were known as A-Team and TeamX.

This was truly the big picture, starting as early in the design process as possible, the exact type of work I desired. I set up a meeting with the Advanced Design Engineering group supervisor, Dr. Jackie Green, to start the "Hire Kevin Chat." I was extremely nervous for this meeting because I needed to rock it (pun intended). I went in expecting to talk about my resume and my work experience, but to my surprise it was nothing like that. I had met this group supervisor briefly in passing before where she actually told me to set up a meeting with her. Jackie is an older woman in her 50's who is still in great shape as a Pilates instructor. She has a vibrant glow about her with brown & blonde long hair and her kindness and considerate manners. I entered her office and sat down ready to go. She asked me to tell her about myself and then it just continued as casual conversation to get to know one another. There was no talk of my resume and she even made a note of that. She said that she wants to get to know someone first, who they are as a person, their interests, and how they would get along with the other group members. She said I was already at JPL so I obviously had some good qualifications to get the internship. This first real meeting was to see if my personality matched what was appropriate for her group.

The group dynamic is extremely important at JPL. Each supervisor I met with mentioned something about it. They wanted to see if I would fit in with the other members, if I would get along and make friends with them. I appreciated this and it did make a lot of sense. I would be working with these people for 40–50 hours a week for the rest of my life. In order to have a happy and productive employee, positive group dynamics must be there.

The "Hire Kevin Chat" with Jackie was going extremely well in terms of conversation and getting along. As we were wrapping up this meeting, Jackie asked me to go and do an exercise that she had the rest of her group do in a group meeting the week before. The exercise was a brain map. A brain map is where you put your name in the middle of a sheet of paper and then place aspects of your life around it, drawing lines between things that interrelate, connecting the aspects. It shows work, life, goals, interests, and more. She explained this concept to me and I enjoyed the idea. To make sure I understood what the task entailed, I mentioned a few examples of what I would put on my brain map. Spoiler alert: Jackie is the group supervisor who ended up hiring me. This is where I believe I truly showed Jackie that I belonged in her group and I think at this moment too she knew she wanted to hire me.

I mentioned that one of my outside-of-work goals what that I was training for my first Men's Physique competition. When I mentioned this, I saw something click with her. I could see it in her facial expression, especially in her eyes. Then her words that followed were even better. She said something very close to "Wow that's it. That is what I am looking for in my group members. The time and dedication it takes to do something like that, those qualities flow into every other aspect of your life; into your work ethic and your career. I, myself, am a Pilates instructor and I see the overlap between fitness and work and how beneficial it is." I replied with "Yes! One of the things that it teaches you, is that sometimes you have to do things you do not want in order to get the end goal that you do want. I do not always feel like working out, but I know that there's an image I have for my body & health that I am going for and exercising will help me achieve that, even if I don't enjoy every workout." She asked me to complete the brain map and come show it to her next week.

I have to be honest here and say that I was waiting to pull out that Men's Physique card at the exact right moment. I was told by others that Jackie was into fitness and most fitness-oriented individuals can almost immediately connect with one another because we know what dedication and sacrifice must go into it. There is immediately respect present when it becomes known.

I completed the brain map and set up another "Hire Kevin Chat." I liked filling out the brain map. It was enjoyable to put everything down on paper and lay it all out. In our second meeting, we discussed the brain map. She said what I created matched extremely well with what an ideal advanced design engineering group member would have. I had phrases like "Explore the unknown" and "Answer the questions we do not have answers for yet" as well as showed links between my fitness habits and work habits. I was feeling extremely positive about my interactions with Jackie and had high hopes. Next she instructed that I talk with another member of the group. She called him over right then and handed my resume to him.

We chatted for a while and everything went smoothly. I knew that he would report back to Jackie about how the chat went and if he saw me as a good fit for the group with a good skill set. He must have given a positive report because soon after Jackie asked me to set up another meeting with her. In this meeting she described what it took for her to hire someone, how she needed to have a work portfolio of tasks that had funding. She then asked me to go and meet with a potential customer, as she called it. It was a JPLer, but the way JPL works is that you have your group supervisor and essentially are "contracted" out to do various tasks. Those tasks have bosses, which are called customers. Jackie told me that I really needed to "hit it outta the ballpark" in this meeting to get things going.

I went to this customer meeting fully alert on a couple cups of coffee and had my notebook and pen in hand. I took several notes during the meeting; catching the buzzwords, software programs, and methods used in this customer's work. The work for this customer did not really interest me, but I knew it would be something to help me get into JPL and then after a little while I could transition to a different task. So at this point, I will admit that I was not 100% honest to the customer who asked if the work interested me. I said that I could be of value to the team and that it was interesting to me. The overall idea of the task was interesting, but the actual work itself was definitely not in my interests.

This customer then wanted me to meet with the other members of the team to see if they liked me and thought I had the skills needed to aide in their assignments. From my notes, I researched the methods and software programs I was unfamiliar with before those meetings. I tried to gain as much knowledge as possible to show that I could hold a conversation about them and relate what I knew. I met with the team members and both thought that I would be a good asset to the team and reported that back to the customer. Goal complete. I knocked those meetings "outta the park" as well and secured a portion of my future work portfolio.

I went back to Jackie and reported the positive outcomes of my meetings. The customer wanted me to do their task 100% of the time when I would become a fulltime JPLer. Since this task was not in my interests, I really did not want to do that. I did not want to do something day in and day out that I really did not like. I relayed this to Jackie and she said she'd see what she could do. I essentially had a job offer at this point if I wanted it, but it was doing something I did not want to do. I've come this far fighting for what I want and I am going to continue to fight until I get what I want. Jackie said that it could drop to 50% of the time, but then she would have to find another 50% for my work portfolio. She sensed my passion for JPL and was willing to help me get what I wanted.

She asked me for a couple more things. She wanted a "one-pager" that was a highlight of my resume and had my picture on it. This was a good tool for her to use to also help build the work portfolio. She also asked if she could get a reference from my graduate school advisor to show my skills and work ethic. I ended getting two references: one from my advisor, Dr. Mavris, and one from my Research Engineer, Stephen Edwards. I was accumulating everything necessary to prove my worth and get hired. These tools were needed to convince the section managers that I should be hired and that there was work for me to be hired to do.

The internship was approaching its end and I was still going through the process to get myself hired. With only two weeks left, I wasn't sure if I would get an offer for the job I wanted in time. I went to my internship boss and we planned to extend my internship by three weeks and started that paperwork. I let Jackie know about this so that she knew what I was doing. She appreciated the effort I was putting in to get myself a job and told me she was still working to see what she could do.

I was invited to a celebration for the Mission Formulation section the next week, which was the last week of my regular 10-week internship. I was not part of Mission Formulation, but of Mission Operations during my internship; two different sections at JPL. While I was at this celebration on the back patio of one of the buildings, Jackie pulled me aside to chat. She asked if I could still undo the three week extension and I said that I'm sure I could since the paperwork was not final yet. In my head, I'm smiling like crazy. She told me to go check and see if I could opt out and then come let her know. I immediately went upstairs to talk to the right people and find out. A quick conversation resulting in me being able to withdraw my internship extension.

When I returned to Jackie to inform her, she said with a big smile on her face "Well maybe you should go home and spend some time with your family. There's nothing to worry about. Everything's good." I knew right there and then that I for sure had a job offer in the works. HR has to make the official offer, which is known to take a while at JPL, so group supervisors cannot directly come out and say you have a job. However, I was told by Jackie in the past that when she decided to hire a friend of mine last year that the only thing she could say to him when he asked about a fulltime job was "There's nothing to worry about, everything's good." So recalling this past moment, I knew with 100% certainty that I was getting a job offer in the following weeks after HR processed all the paperwork.

I felt an immediate achievement. I could not wait to tell my family and friends. I quickly found my friends who were already full time JPL employees and told them about it. I was anxious to get out of work and call my family. I called home with excitement and told them the great news. They were overjoyed and said they were proud of me. The first thing my mother asked was if I had the paperwork. I said no and that HR had to do some processing, but I explained the words from Jackie that meant it was surely coming. She seemed slightly timid, but I had complete faith that it would come.

I figured out my arrangements to head back to Wisconsin and spend some time with my family while I awaited the official offer. I would not fly out for another week after my internship ended because I had one more activity to complete at JPL before I left. I was accepted into Planetary Science Summer School (PSSS) which occurred during the week after my internship ended.

Achieving a 15 Year Dream

PLANETARY SCIENCE SUMMER School, known as PSSS, is a one week course at JPL in which a team of students learn the mission planning and life cycle process of mission concepts. A mission concept is taken through a concurrent engineering environment and the members of the advanced engineering design team mentors the students. This advanced design team is known as "TeamX" which is the team I would actually be joining once I started up my full time role at JPL; more about that later on. A brief intro to Planetary Science Summer School (PSSS) per the website:

> "PSSS prepares the next generation of engineers and scientists to participate in future solar system exploration missions. Participants learn the mission life cycle, roles of scientists and engineers in a mission environment, mission design interconnectedness and trade-offs, and the importance of teamwork".

The main eligibility requirements to get into PSSS were stated as being either a postdoc, recent PhD, or an in-work PhD student. There was a small footnote that stated engineering students who are in their Master's program are eligible. However, the application process does give priority to the PhD holders and PhD candidates. I applied the year before and did not get accepted, but one of my friends at Georgia Tech did. For this second try, he put in a good word for me and I received the acceptance letter for summer 2014.

There is actually a lot of prep work that goes into PSSS by us students. We had ten weeks leading up to it where we had a weekly webinar. During these webinars, we selected the mission and science goals from the Decadal Survey. The Decadal Survey is a ranking of science priority items by the scientific community. We also chose what instrumentation we would like to have on the spacecraft and started to do research as well as assign roles for the team. I was given three roles: Mechanical Engineer, Geology Scientist, and Gravity Science Lead.

The mechanical engineer would be my role in the concurrent engineering environment with TeamX where I would work with an expert to design our system. I was a geologist for my science role to learn what geology was important to study in order to answer the questions the Decadal Survey posed. Lastly I was the gravity science lead, which was my instrumentation position. I chose gravity science based on my internship experience and thought I could provide benefit to the team with my knowledge on the subject.

Our mission concept was to Enceladus, one of Saturn's moons. It is the moon that has plumes or geysers erupting from its South Polar Terrain which actually forms the E-Ring of Saturn. We debated between an orbiter, a flyby, a sample return, and a lander mission. We ultimately chose the orbiter mission as it was the best function to achieve the science information that we desired. Our spacecraft was to be powered by solar panels, something that has never been done that far out in the solar system, but with the improving technology we believed we could do it by the time we needed to launch. The most constraining part of this design process was to make it fit under the cost cap; that is to be affordable. We wanted to do so much with it, but NASA would only allow us to use so much money. We were acting as a New Frontiers class mission which is approximately $1 billion. We came in well over the cost cap with our first design. We shot for the ideal situation hoping it would fit, but then we had to descope, and descope again, until our design was feasible against all requirements.

Once all the students gathered at JPL for the week, we essentially worked from 8am to midnight each day to get our work done. It was an exhausting, but valuable experience. At the end of the week we had to present our concept study results to a proposal review board which consisted of JPL scientists and engineers as well as NASA Headquarters executives. They provided feedback on our results and stated what strengths and weaknesses they saw in our concept proposal. It was an amazing experience and a great crash course for what was to come in my future job. I was excited to start doing this type of activity on a regular basis and it would not require the 16-hour shift schedule as we would have more time to complete these tasks. The week was over and now it was time to head home to Wisconsin and await the official offer from JPL.

The Call, Finally

I was excited to see my family and friends again for a little bit while I was waiting for JPL's HR to do its work. I took off towards LAX to leave sunny California and go back to humid Wisconsin for a few weeks. When I arrived at LAX, it was busier than I had ever seen it and I had a bag to check. I ended up missing my flight because it took too long to check my bags. Time to be a problem solver, so I headed to the desk and spoke with an attendant. He booked me on a flight to Denver instead of my connecting flight through Las Vegas without any issue. However, when I arrived in Denver I had nowhere to go. I went to the gate of my connecting flight to Wisconsin and it was already overbooked. Time to be a problem solver again. The next flight to Wisconsin wasn't until the next morning. I was stranded in Denver without any luggage. I found a hotel, bought a toothbrush, and grabbed some food. A slight hiccup, but I eventually got home.

Each day that passed I was becoming more and more anxious to get the official word. It was two weeks now at this point and I was feeling slightly worried that something may have gone wrong. I emailed Jackie and told her I had not yet received the call and she responded with "Just be patient, everything is good." So with that reassurance I felt better and decided to take some action to prepare for the move. I condensed and organized all my belongings that were to go from my parent's house. My friends at JPL told me that the relocation package was pretty nice. JPL will pay for a moving company to come, pack up all my stuff, ship it out to LA, and even store it up to 60 days if needed. A pretty good deal if I do say so myself.

JPL will also put you up in a Residence Inn for 60 days if you didn't find a place to live from a paid trip out to LA to house hunt. I was planning on staying at the same location I lived during my internship. So I opted out of that opportunity, but again, it was a pretty good deal. JPL's relocation package was one of the best that I've heard of. I even got a $2,500 miscellaneous expense stipend for the move as well. The last part of the package was that JPL would either ship your car and fly you out or pay for your gas and hotels along the road trip if you so desired. I did not own a car at the moment, I had been renting one while I was in LA. Since I had some time on my hands, I figured it would be smart to spend this time searching for, test driving, and buying a car instead of attempting to do that during my full time job once I moved to California.

I knew exactly where I was going for that, no question about it. I think it stems from the Transporter movies with Jason Statham actually. I loved the car in those movies. I went to my sister and said "Hey, you want to go test drive Audi's with me?" She of course said yes and happily came along. We went to the Audi dealership in Appleton and I was like a kid in a candy store. This was going to be my present to myself for all the hardships and obstacles I overcame to achieve my JPL job. Overcoming this much adversity deserves an award! There was a lot of searching, test driving, and looking around to find the right car and at a good deal.

The first car the salesman had me test drive was a TT. It's a small coupe sports car that I did not think I would even fit in. I did, mostly, and he had me drive the heck out of it to get me fired up. This one was definitely out of my price range coming in at over $70,000. I wasn't looking to break the bank and go overboard. I wanted a nice solid car that I could fit into the budget. I did some math and figured out what the price range of payments I could make would be with my soon-to-be salary. I test drove multiple A3's, S3's, A4's, and A6's.

I really fell in love with a cherry red 2016 S4 with the black optics package. It had the race car seat and driver's wheel, paddle shifters on the steering wheel, black interior, and a large sunroof. It was a sleek ride that also pushed the budget too tight. I ultimately decided on a 2014 A4 S-Line with one previous owner and 12,000 miles. I did some negotiating to bring down the price a few thousand dollars and even got them to throw in a roof rack for free to put a cherry on top of the deal.

About a week before I actually decided on the Audi and signed the paperwork, my phone rang one afternoon. I was sitting at the kitchen counter and my mom was in the living room relaxing in her recliner. Her recliner was my favorite spot to take a nap when I was home. I rarely take naps, but the comfort of that thing is unbeatable. I answered the phone and said "Hi this is Kevin" to then hear a response of "Hi Kevin, this is Mario from NASA JPL." At this point I jumped up, went into my mom's line of sight, waved my hands smiling and pointed to phone mouthing the words "IT'S JPL!!" She immediately got up and came over to try and listen in. I took a bunch of notes of what the offer was, who my HR contacts were, and what the relocation package contained; all the details I could scratch down. The end of the conversation consisted of "Do you accept this offer?" and I replied with a resounding "YES SIR!" As much as I knew from others at JPL, there really was not much negotiating power for new hires right out of college. Especially if I didn't have another job offer on the table for them to compete with. I did not attempt to alter the terms.

As soon as I hung up my mom gave me a huge hug, said congratulations, and then scurried away quickly to the garage and said "Hold on." She came back with a mini bottle of champagne. I had been without a drop of alcohol for three months at this time and did not plan on breaking my streak (I am more than four years now as I write this). I politely declined to toast with the champagne, but instead with the coffee I had. She popped open the bottle, we cheered and celebrated. My 15-year long dream job of becoming a NASA Rocket Scientist was officially accomplished.

PART 2

...AND BEYOND

15

Living the Dream

YOU WOULD THINK that would be an end to the story of
persevering through adversity, but this story is actually just
beginning (as we're 13 chapters in...trust me I'll make it quick.
Be on the lookout for book #2 someday). I landed my 15-year
long dream job and I was living the dream. I bought my dream
car, an Audi, a black 2014 A4 S-line Premium Plus trim with
the Bang-Olufsen sound system and I called her Athena. I
even ordered personalized license plates that read RCKT SCI.
I was working in the Advanced Design Engineering group as
a Systems Engineer. I was officially part of the TeamX staff I
had experienced just a few weeks earlier. Over the course of a
year and a half, I was involved in over 30 different spacecraft
concept designs from orbiting the earth to exploring the
universe. I worked on concepts to study the sun, the earth,
a sample return from the moon, from mars, from asteroids,
looking to the outer planets and moons in our solar system,
and even telescopes to look beyond into the depths of the
universe. It was a rapid pace, team environment that was
exciting and always different.

As refresher from Part 1: TeamX is an advanced design engineering team that utilizes concurrent engineering. Concurrent engineering is engineering done in parallel instead of in series. The historic design process is that one person does work and gives their results to another for their work via email, paper, or word of mouth. This process continues on for the next person to do their work on a project. Concurrent engineering has all the members of the team in the same room at the same time to get everyone on the same page, have the right conversations together, answer questions as a team, and converge quickly on a design.

TeamX holds design sessions that are each three hours in duration for a mission concept. Each concept will have between on average three or four sessions to complete what is called a Study. A group of experts in several disciplines gather in a room with computers all linked up together via a special type of intranet—a software environment developed by JPL specifically for this team and its processes. The group of experts was selected based on what type of mission was being done and how much information was going to be needed to complete the study. Experts came from Science, Instruments, Command & Data Handling, Software, Telecommunications, Ground Data Systems, ATLO, Planetary Protection, Thermal, Power, Mechanical, Configuration, Attitude Control, Propulsion, Mission Design, Trajectory/Visualization, EDL (Entry Descent, Landing), Programmatics/Risk, Cost, and my role Systems Engineering.

Studies were held for everything, looking at single missions, campaigns, and spacecraft constellations. The missions were diverse: investigating earth, planetary missions, lunar, astrophysics, heliophysics, and human. Numerous different types of flight systems were able to be studied: orbiters, rovers, landers, aerobots, submersibles, and sample returns. The missions looked at remote sensing of science and in-situ science investigations. TeamX tackled every sort of mission concept that was out there or still yet to be defined. The team used historical design data and mass estimating relationships to build models to use as design tools. These design tools were all tied together with automatic construction of technical resources shared between the disciplines. Meaning one person's outputs were another person's inputs, they are automatically sent through the software system to enable this sharing. This empowered the generation of rapid turnaround, innovative space mission concepts.

TeamX and its environment were great for spacecrafts that were similar in size and mass to what had been done before, but there was a new type of spacecraft coming into the market— the CubeSat. CubeSats are small, modular spacecrafts that range from 10-cm x 10-cm x 10-cm blocks to ones the size of briefcases. With improved technology, a smaller spacecraft could be built to do some of the things the larger ones did. CubeSats were up and coming and the advanced design engineering team needed to get on board. So with that, TeamXc was spun up. It was a similar team with different design models and different experts that were knowledgeable in CubeSats and their capabilities. I was part of this team as well. I eventually became the lead for a software overhaul, orchestrating the transition, but then an opportunity arose that I needed to take advantage of.

I was offered a position on the Europa Lander team at NASA JPL. If you recall, Europa is my baby. It was my first experience with NASA JPL as my graduate school research work and also my 10-week internship that lead to my job. I knew Europa better than any other body in the solar system, besides earth of course. I ended up splitting my time 50-50 between TeamX/ Xc and Europa Lander for about six months. However, each team was giving me tasks as if I was 100% with them and it was getting to be too much on my plate. I spoke with several people around JPL about my situation and asked for advice. I enjoyed both teams, but did not have the bandwidth to support them both the way they wanted. Through these conversations, it was largely skewed towards leaving TeamX and giving all of my time to Europa Lander. This way I would get "flight project credibility" which is well respected for career advancement and I would get deep down into the weeds of the design instead of just skimming the surface rapidly with TeamX. A going down in the trenches of the design if you will.

My role was a member of the Europa Lander Flight System Systems Engineering team. I'm about to get uber technical and use a bunch of jargon so bear with me over the next few paragraphs as I describe what I did and was responsible for.

I created and owned the System Model in a program called MagicDraw, the PEL (Power Equipment List), the power modes in mission phases, and the resource allocations across all four spacecraft elements: Lander, Descent Stage, DeOrbit Stage (managed by NASA Marshall Space Flight Center), Cruise Stage (managed by the Applied Physics Lab) as well as a co-organizer of CAE (computer aided engineer) involvement and the director & developer of the new MEL (mass equipment list) process.

I used MBSE (model-based systems engineering) to create and maintain a system model that served as an authoritative-source-of-truth. It was a computer environment for the PEL, Power/Thermal resources design, and Flight System block diagrams that consisted of MagicDraw, Excel, Tom Sawyer Perspectives, Jython & VBA (visual basic for applications) scripting. I was the sole modeler of the system model in MagicDraw and generated reports in Excel for the team to view. Scripts, or custom computer code, were used to extract the model information. It would transplant it into Excel to be automatically formatted and analyzed with VBA.

The PEL is an interactive Excel sheet whose values can be pulled back into the system model if there are changes made in the Excel file. I also automated the building of power mode scenarios for different phases in Excel. They are built directly from the Excel PEL and can also be updated automatically with a click of a button if there are architectural changes made to the PEL.

I was co-leading an effort with another member of the team incorporating a CAE member into the Europa Lander Team—we orchestrated the involvement and had status/progress meetings bi-weekly to advance the CAE & modeling efforts of the Lander design in a Lab supported fashion. Specifically leading efforts for automatic block diagramming and power scenario information storage. The resource lists (switches, heaters, thermal zones, pyrotechnic devices, motors, propulsion drivers, computer card counts) are built in and exported from the system model to be viewed in Excel as well.

Europa Lander desired a new process for updating, reviewing, & maintaining the MEL for a multi-segment spacecraft in conceptual design. So I lead and prototyped the new MEL framework being developed using Excel as the user interface, Python as the connecting glue, and GitHub as the version control & tracking feature. The MEL process will take several subsystem MELs in their own Excel sheets, version them via text file in GitHub, & compile them into a System MEL with roll-ups and system summaries that feed further analysis. Versioning, or tracking the different iterations, of the compiled System MEL is also done with a convenient way to view the changes from one version to another. Additional investigation for future integration with mass properties is being done consulting with the mechanical engineering team along the way.

Whew, okay we're done with the jargon for now. Basically I was a space systems engineer integrating spacecrafts by implementing paradigm shifting design methodologies utilizing model-based systems engineering (MBSE). Another mouthful, yeah I'm sorry, but it IS rocket science. :)

I spent some of my free time early on engaging in public outreach where I wrote to students, presented to children, and gave private guided tours of NASA JPL. The feeling of satisfaction and fulfillment that came from each of these experiences is indescribable with words. I have tried and just nothing can do it justice. I craved this, I wanted more of it, the feeling of educating and inspiring others touched my soul on the deepest of levels. I became the most active member of the NASA JPL Speakers Bureau, an organization that fulfilled speaking requests that came into the lab. I spoke to audiences of all ages: preschoolers, elementary and middle school classrooms and science nights, high school auditoriums, college career fairs, and professional international symposiums. I even organized, set up, and hosted my own NASA JPL booth for a Boy Scout Youth S.T.E.M. Expo where I didn't leave the table for eight hours. In my first year alone I spoke to over 60,000 individuals in person. I would skype with classrooms and students around the world. I even traveled to South Korea during the summers to teach a space camp at the SongAm Observatory. My life outside of the office was anything but dull.

Fit Rocket Scientist

I'VE ALWAYS BEEN a fitness nut. I didn't make my college soccer team so I turned into a "meathead" for six years lifting weights and doing bodybuilding. Not making the soccer team was a big surprise for me. I was my high school team captain for two years, I took my team to state my Junior year for the first time in school history, I was given All-State & All-Conference awards, I was dual MVP, overall and defensive, for two years, and I had multiple colleges recruiting me, however these colleges didn't have engineering. That's a story for a different time. I had a sport hole to fill so I fell in love with the weight room. I worked out all the time, loving the feeling of the pump (fullness of muscles), the rush of endorphins, and the results that I saw. It made me feel good and it filled the empty feeling I had from not playing soccer anymore. Not playing soccer allowed me to build some muscle and put on some size since I wasn't conditioning all the time. Not making the team was a blessing in disguise as it allowed me to focus more on my studies. I witnessed my friends who did make the team get absorbed more by being a soccer player than a college student and their studies greatly suffered.

I can confidently say that if I did make the team I would not have achieved my dream of working for NASA.

I was asked quite frequently through graduate school why I wasn't pursuing personal training or some type of fitness career instead of aerospace. Several people requested that I build them workout and/or diet programs. I was up at 5am to walk to the gym, about two miles from my apartment, to get in as soon as it opened so I could get in my workouts before my classes and research took over the day. I was diligent. I made meals for the week on Sundays and planned everything out from macros (carbs, fats, protein) to what specific exercises and number of sets and repetitions I would do. I carried around a gallon of water to make sure I would finish it and then some each day. Having this consistent exercise regimen is what allowed me to survive graduate school and be even more efficient and productive. My mind was clear, I had energy, my body and mind were operating like a well-oiled machine.

If I was up against a wall in my research or coursework and not able to figure something out, I had two options. One, I could keep on pushing through and maybe solve it in four-to-six hours. Or two, I could take an hour break, go for a run or lift weights, to come back and solve the problem in one-to-two hours. The incorporation of exercise consistently in my life allowed me to think clearly, escape the problem, and reset to come back full boar to tackle grad school challenges. This is true in all aspects of life. A consistent exercise regimen and healthy eating style will benefit you physically, mentally, and emotionally in your career, relationships, and personal lifestyle. It has continued to do amazing things for me.

I always saw fitness as a hobby that was inferior to aerospace. I also used fitness as my outlet for stress relief in my life and I was hesitant to make my stress-reliever a potential stress-inducer. I happily made programs for my friends who asked and answered any questions I received in-person or via social media. Having achieved my dream of a NASA Rocket Scientist, I now wanted to take time to share my fitness knowledge with everyone. I studied and passed the exam to be a National Academy of Sports Medicine (NASM) Certified Personal Trainer (CPT). I wanted to have some credibility next to my name and have increased confidence and knowledge in my answers to helping others. I felt quite confident as I studied and took the test for I already knew a lot of the information from my own research over the years. There is a lot of misleading information on the internet and in conversations with avid gym goers, but this showed me that I was able to sort through most of the inaccuracies and come to the correct conclusions.

I wanted a brand for myself in the fitness industry. I first used AeroAesthetics as a call sign, but then decided to call myself the *Fit Rocket Scientist*. I wanted a logo for this brand, so I reached out to my best friend Brandon who is a graphic designer. I was looking for a logo that encompassed the rocket scientist aspect of my life to set me apart in the fitness world. We iterated for about a year on the logo with different ideas and designs before it became final. I am not good at drawing whatsoever, but I attempted to put pen to paper to give Brandon an idea of what was floating around in my head. You'll be able to see the clear difference of my first two drawings and then Brandon's handiwork to follow. (You are able to see these images on *www.tonasaandbeyond.com/images*)

I loved Brandon's work. I wanted to show more of the fitness side in my logo because I think that is a unique aspect to the rocket scientist and here is where the *Fit* in *Fit Rocket Scientist* officially became part of the brand. I had an idea for a logo, what if there was a rocket that was a person with abs and muscles. I attempted to draw this out and sent it to Brandon. It really looks like a lobster, I'm a terrible artist, but he turned it into something spectacular.

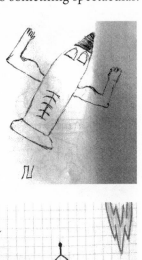

I used this logo for everything. I had die-cut business cards and stickers made. I put it in the bottom corner of every YouTube video I made. I created t-shirts with the logo on it to wear in videos, while working out in public, and to sell on my website at the time *www.FitRocketScientist.com* as well. I am so proud of it. It is essentially me in cartoon form, how fun! On my website I had exercise programs, nutrition information, supplement explanations, and a blog about common and unknown health topics.

One of my goals for fitness was to be with a supplement company and be on the other side of the booth at expos. I would go to fitness conventions and go through collecting information, supplement samples, and meeting athletes sponsored by those companies. Going through these expos I desired to be one of those athletes, to be a role model and figure of inspiration on the platform of a well-known company. I achieved part of this goal, not being sponsored, but I ended up working with a supplement company known as Beast Sports Nutrition as a demo rep for about six months. I would go to nutrition stores and set up a table to give out samples of products to customers and teach them about supplements. I then staffed the booth at the LA Fit Expo—check that goal box!

I ended up leaving this company because their brand vision and image did not quite align with the brand image and vision I had for *Fit Rocket Scientist*. I also saw that most of what I was witnessing and desiring as a sponsored-athlete with these companies was a facade, it wasn't really real or what people think it is. Getting more involved in the supplement industry as a demo rep opened my eyes to this and my desire to become a supplement company sponsored athlete was no more. I wanted to do my own thing, be my own brand, and have control over everything I did.

YouTube and Instagram were my main platforms for informing about fitness. I created a YouTube series called "30 Seconds to…" where I made 30-second videos to introduce a topic and give a brief description of what it was. I saw myself as seeking quick information videos and not to waste my time watching something for three-to-five minutes since I'm always busy. I saw a good opportunity to create a bunch of 30-second videos to serve the purpose of quick on-the-go information. I also created workout videos, meal prep videos, nutrition planning, and supplementation videos. I started vlogging and that turned into a weekly occurrence posting a vlog every Monday. This gave me a ton of experience in front of a camera to get myself more experienced and comfortable with what is yet to come.

I did a Men's Physique show at Muscle Beach in Venice, CA (this is the one I told Jackie I was training for—side note: she gathered a bunch of coworkers and came out to watch me compete, what a boss!). From that competition, I really learned that I didn't feel athletic anymore. I looked great, but I felt like an ornament that couldn't do anything. I wanted to be an athlete again, use my body as a tool to do things. In the same week I had these thoughts, I signed up for three Spartan Races, a Tough Mudder, and applied to compete on American Ninja Warrior. I was still in love with fitness, but needed to change it up to be more of a lifestyle fitness approach.

I started going to a climbing gym and found an American Ninja Warrior backyard course. I also got into doing daily yoga and reduced how many days I was just lifting weights. Ninja obstacles are all so hard and unique which is unlike anything I had ever done before. I felt like the big dumb muscle guy at the climbing gyms who just tried to muscle his way through the routes, but I was trying to learn technique and the proper approach. It was a puzzle to solve and I liked that aspect.

The backyard American Ninja Warrior course was called 323 Ninja Training Grounds and was operated by a ninja named Arnold Hernandez. He built the course in his backyard and I found his place through Facebook. I went there to film part of my application video and man…were those the hardest exercises I ever attempted. It was so unique, so difficult. There was so much room for improvement here and I dug in.

I found a service called ROMWOD, which stands for Range Of Motion Workout Of the Day, for my daily yoga exercises. I heard about it from one of the fitness professionals I looked up to and was following through social media. ROMWOD would provide 14–20 minute videos every single day taking you through a variety of poses and breathing exercises. I felt so awkward, so inflexible, so much that in the beginning I only did it alone in my apartment.

Instead of going to the weight room six or seven days a week, I started to incorporate trail runs and bodyweight interval exercises into my weekly training. I lived right next to the Arroyo in Altadena, CA near the foothills of the San Gabriel Mountains. Trail running was easily available and plentiful.

About three months later I got the call from the producers of American Ninja Warrior that I was chosen to be a competitor for the Los Angeles Qualifiers. The application process is about a ten page online application full of questions and then a 2–3 minutes video submission. I submitted my application back in November and sat in limbo wondering if I would be selected, not knowing when that would actually come. It was early February and I figured that since the competition was just over a month away, if I was going to be selected I would already have been notified. So I assumed I didn't make it and said "oh well, I tried."

The experience was amazing! Unfortunately, I did not get to hit a buzzer as I failed the third obstacle. About 100 competitors run the course in each city, but they only show about 30–40 on tv. Luckily my run was aired and everyone got to see me compete on Season 9. I continued to train and applied again for Season 10. I got selected! I competed in LA, but once again failed the third obstacle (not the same one, they are different every year) and did not get to hit a buzzer and advance to the next stage of obstacles. I am still training and working to improve my ninja abilities. It's so much fun, like adult jungle gyms! The ninja community is like a family too. I have made some great friends. It is such a great environment to be a part of.

17

My New Trajectory

I **FOUND MYSELF** becoming increasingly unfulfilled with my work at NASA JPL. It took me a while to figure out why. Yes, I was working on a spacecraft that could possibly launch one day (it was a concept mission aimed to launch in seven years), and inspire millions of people, but I am so far disconnected from those individuals. I realized I want to be on the front lines educating and inspiring people firsthand. I believe that I have a unique set of skills that allow me to communicate and be relatable to the general public about space. I then had an idea. The current population, especially today's youth, lack exposure to space science and the marvelous machines that explore outer space. Millennials grew up learning from Bill Nye the Science Guy, Neil deGrasse Tyson, & Stephen Hawking. The generation before learned from Mr. Wizard & Carl Sagan. The public needs a new, young, space expert and enthusiast that is more relatable to reignite the excitement and teach the younger generation.*

---

* As I've gone down this path, I've met so many wonderful individuals involved with space education!

There needs to be an increase in exposure to space exploration and its aide in technology development. I've been doing that on a small scale for years now and it was the most rewarding part of my life. What if I could do that on a much grander scale?

I can be that individual, no, I NEED to be that individual. I have a young, charismatic character and the ability to simplify concepts for understanding by all ages and backgrounds. I am not your stereotypical engineer or scientist. I'm an extroverted, goofy, funny, and athletic individual who can draw in an audience. I am a rocket scientist & fitness addict who teaches the public about space and promotes living an active & healthy lifestyle. I had previously created a brand for myself, *Fit Rocket Scientist*, and I added to it. Now *Fit Rocket Scientist* was about being the first Kevin J. DeBruin—the source of information for all things space and an advocate for a healthy lifestyle on earth. I educate about space in a fun & easy to understand way. And at the same time serving as a role model by showcasing an active & healthy lifestyle with grit & determination. I break the traditional stereotypes of dumb-jock and socially awkward nerd.

Now I understand that this may come off that I'm arrogant to think I am deserving of such an honor—however, that is not my intention or directive. I recognize the aspects that I've come to possess. I do not want to brag about them, but acknowledge how I can use them for good as I feel the most fulfilled when I am helping and teaching others. I encourage everyone to discover the unique aspects they can bring to the table for the betterment of others. I craved being of service to others more and more. I believe that I can help bring good change in the world with the skills I have developed and things I have experienced. When I had this realization, I felt like it was a calling, a destiny. It's my new trajectory, the next path I must pave.

At this time, I came up with a mission:

1. Expose and educate the public about space science.
2. Promote an active and healthy lifestyle.
3. Endorse living a grateful and thankful life.
4. Inspire others by sharing my own experiences to show nothing is impossible.

Everything I did related to one or more of these mission statements. I strived to hit as many of them as once as possible. All of my social media posts and public appearances were rooted in these words. This is what kept me grounded and focused on the right path as I moved forward with my brand.

I created YouTube videos and became part of the LA Public Library S.T.E.A.M. speaker series. I made YouTube videos talking about space concepts that everyone could understand. I broke down the complex concepts into every day references that people could relate to. I slowly improved my content and even took a trip to Hawaii to film a four-part science series about the wonderful science of Hawaii. For the LA Public Library, I had to audition. I created a program where I taught about the solar system using inflatable planets and made soda-straw rockets with kids and parents. I passed the audition with flying colors and still speak at libraries all over Los Angeles.

I decided to strategize my Instagram. I would post three posts a day, to keep a clear vision on my profile. One post would be about space: images of a star/planet, a view from the International Space Station, a look into past/present/future spacecraft and technology, and an easy to understand explanation. One post would be an accountability post for health & fitness: a current progress picture of me shirtless taken in the morning combined with a caption providing tips, giving motivation, or insight into my own current training and nutrition. Finally, yet importantly, one post would show me enjoying life, going on adventures, being grateful, or living an active and healthy lifestyle. To sum it up, this post would have my face in it. I did this for an entire year, and then some.

Throughout this time I gained a solid amount of followers and to each one of my new followers I reached out. I sent a message thanking them for following me, personalizing it with their name, and then asking what they followed for: space, fitness, or my smile. I surveyed every new follower for over a year and the dominant response was space, followed by all three. I decided to go all in on the space aspect and embody the image and brand of *Fit Rocket Scientist* in my physical appearance. I went through a rebranding of myself to be known as *Kevin J DeBruin* as I wanted to be a source of information for space. *Fit Rocket Scientist* and the buff rocket logo is great to set myself apart in the fitness world, but it can be a hindrance going forward in space education. I'm moving forward as *Kevin J DeBruin*, but I'm still known as the *Fit Rocket Scientist* to many which I will always keep with me. *Kevin J DeBruin*, a.k.a. *Fit Rocket Scientist*, is here to teach you about space!

Growing up, my generation learned from Bill Nye the Science guy. The generation before me had Carl Sagan. I believe it is my duty to carry the baton and continue the legacy of teaching space and inspiring the youth. After three years of working at NASA, I have left to take on being a Space Educator full time. As I have my own style, I, the first *Kevin J DeBruin*, will continue to inspire and educate those around me.

ACKNOWLEDGEMENTS

To the individual reading this, I appreciate you.

Thank you to all those who have inspired
and aided me in my journey.

Special thanks to reviews and edits by
TJ, Andrew, Ashleigh, and Ron.

Special thanks to Sebastian for assistance in cover design.

Special thanks to James for aiding in
recording the audiobook.

The utmost appreciation for my loving partner. Brittany,
who gave me support and encouragement throughout
the publishing process and helping with the editing.

Made in the USA
Coppell, TX
12 March 2021